PEOPLE FROM THE SKY

Told by Frances Carpenter

Illustrated by Betty Fraser

Doubleday & Company, Inc.
Garden City, New York

1972

PEOPLE
FROM
THE SKY
Ainu Tales
from
Northern
Japan

ACKNOWLEDGMENTS

The Ainu tales in this book have come from many sources, especially from writings of the nineteenth century. Special mention should be made of the following:

Reverend John Batchelor, The Ainu of Japan, 1892; The Ainu and their Folklore, 1901; Ainu Life and Lore, 1902. Basil Hall Chamberlain, Things Japanese, 1890. Chamberlain and Batchelor, First Memoir of the Literature College of the Imperial University of Japan, 1887. Isabella L. Bird, Unbeaten Tracks in Japan, vol. II, 1881. Edward Greey, The Bear Worshippers of Yezo.

Mention should also be made of Ainu Legends (in Japanese) author unknown, which were translated for the author by Simon Virgo, Tokyo.

IN THIS BOOK

Soon there will be no old people like "Ekashi," the chief of the model village on Hokkaido, who remember just how it used to be in Ainu Land. They will all have gone to join their ancestors in the Sky Country of their gods.

So it seems good to set down in this book, some of their ancient wonder tales. It seems good, also, to give Ekashi's memories of how it was here on Japan's northern island of Hokkaido when he was a boy.

On these pages there will be found stories of happenings which he might well have seen with his own eyes; also some of the fabulous myths which could have been handed down to him by his own grandfather. Many of these tell of the Ainu's "Great-and-Important God," and of the "smaller gods" who helped him rule the world. Others describe the lively roles played by animals in the ancient beliefs of Japan's aborigines.

CONTENTS

PEOPLE FROM THE SKY

PEOPLE FROM THE SKY

The Old Man was telling the story to his grand-children—to Toki, the boy, and Haruko, the girl. The two children were squatting on their heels beside him, close to the fire-hole in the earth floor of the big room.

The warmth from the burning wood there was welcome. A biting wind was whistling about the reed walls of the house and over its steep roof of thatch. Cold weather, as usual, had arrived early on this northern Japanese island of Hokkaido.

"Our very first ancestor came down out of the sky," the Old Man was saying. He nodded his head as he spoke. "It was at the beginning, at the very beginning of all things. The Great-and-Important God, who rules all the smaller gods, had set the land down, here and there, on the ocean. He had fitted the hills and the valleys together. He had made the rivers to wind their ways through the forests and across the plains to the sea.

"Fish swam in the waters of the earth. Birds flew through the air. The bear and the deer roamed over the hillsides. It was a beautiful world, more beautiful even than the shining Sky Country where the gods lived.

"But there were no people! No people at all!" The Old Man shook his head. His deep-set brown eyes were bright as he told Toki and Haruko how—as he believed—their world might have come into being. This Ainu grandfather knew many legends about its

creation. But this was the ancient tale he liked best. "One day," he went on, "a great beam of light reached down out of the sky. Along it, riding upon a bright cloud, came the first living person to set foot on the earth. The Great-and-Important God had molded this man's body out of smooth clay. He had given him a strong backbone of willow wood which would bend easily as he moved. Thick, wavy black hair fell to his shoulders. A magnificent black beard covered the lower half of his ruddy face. Oh, that man was truly a fit father for the human race."

The Old Man rose to his feet. He stood very straight, and he raised his arms toward the pointed roof, high over his head. Now he was pretending to be this first ancestor of his people.

"In my mind I am standing on the hill where he did. I am on the very same spot in the Saru Valley where the tablet says he came down out of the sky. And I speak as he did.

"'I am The Ainu!* I am The Man!' Our ancestor shouted the words. They rang out, clear on the air. The birds and the beasts and the fishes all heard them."

The Old Man lowered his arms. With his right hand he slowly stroked his bushy gray beard. This was the favorite gesture of old Ainu men. With it they gave courteous greetings to friends. Or they used it to show that what they were saying was important.

Toki and Haruko admired their grandfather's beard. It was the fullest and longest beard they ever had seen. On their island of Hokkaido, wavy hair and thick beards set the Ainu apart from their straight-haired, smooth-skinned Japanese neighbors. Ainu men had patches of long hair on their chests and their shoulders. Hair covered their legs and their arms. There was hair on the backs of their hands and their fingers.

* Pronounced "eye-noo"

In their hairiness, the Ainu were more like men in Europe, Australia and America, than like those of the chief races of the Far East. It was because of this difference that they have sometimes been called "the hairy Ainu."

4

*People
from the Sky
Ainu Tales
from
Northern
Japan*

Toki and Haruko thought that perhaps his beard was one reason why their grandfather had been put in charge of the model Ainu village of which the big reed house was a part. With his shock of gray hair and his beautiful beard, he was an example of how an Ainu elder should look.

Also the Old Man was wise. He remembered well days gone by. He was an excellent choice to tell visitors about these reed houses which showed how the Ainu lived in the past. Everyone gave him the honorable title of "Ekashi" which was kept for the chief of the village.

"Once, long ago," Ekashi told the children, "our island was known as Yezo, instead of Hokkaido. At that time there were many thousand Ainus in the world. Our people had homes also in the southern Japanese island of Honshu, and on other islands nearby. But the Japanese made war on our ancestors. Their sharp swords and spears, and later their guns, were far better weapons than our arrows and clubs.

"The fierce Japanese pushed our people to the north. They followed us across the water to this island of Yezo. They took over our land. The Ainu fought bravely, but at last we were conquered. There were marriages between the conquerors and our people. To-day there are only a very few of us left whose fore-fathers were pure Ainu.

"The ways of the past are almost forgotten now," Ekashi shook his head. "Only old people like your grandmother and me, remember how life on this is-land used to be. We think it is good to have model villages like this one where people of today can see real Ainu houses. Here visitors from near and far can hear us sing our old songs and tell the old tales. They can watch us step through the ancient dances of our forefathers."

The children's grandmother, Ekashi's wife, was a pure Ainu like him. The old woman's tattooing made this plain to everyone. The marks around her mouth made her look as if she had a huge blue-black mustache. Patterns of tattoo lines covered her arms and her hands.

"When I was young," she told Haruko, "every girl in Ainu Land knew she must be tattooed. It hurt to be pricked with the needle-sharp knife point so that the blue dye would sink in. But it was done little by little, over many years. When it was finished a girl was known to be grown up and ready to marry."

Haruko could well believe that her grandmother's tattooing had hurt. She was glad the Japanese governors of her land had long ago forbidden the custom.

Toki and Haruko were used to the blue marks on their grandmother's skin. They thought she was fine-looking in spite of them, and they loved her dearly. Their name for her was "Fuchi," or Fire, which also was the name for the most beloved goddess of their people. The Fire Goddess was the Grandmother-Goddess, who lived in their fire-hole and looked after their comfort.

Benri, the father of these two children, was the son of Ekashi and Fuchi. His long black hair was wavy and thick. His dark beard was heavy. He was a typical Ainu, and perhaps one day he would take his father's place as head of this model village. On the other hand the children's mother, Tano, was the daughter of two Japanese parents.

Toki looked like his father. His brown eyes were

6

*People
from the Sky
Ainu Tales
from
Northern
Japan*

round, and his skin had a ruddy, tanned glow. Haruko was more like her pretty Japanese mother. Her eyes were set between narrow lids, and her smooth skin was the color of deep cream. Like most descendants of that very first man who came down out of the sky, these two children were only part Ainu.

The real home of this family was very different from the big reed houses in the Ainu village. At some distance away, along a paved highway, they had a modern wooden dwelling with windows of glass. A television aerial rose over its roof. Wires brought electricity in for their lights and their radio. Many of their toys were like those of children in other parts of the world. Toki's most cherished possession was a new plastic space helmet. He had learned about astronauts in his Japanese school.

Each day Benri and Tano, the parents of Toki and Haruko, came to the Ainu village. In the line of tourist booths along the road in from the highway, they had a workshop. Here Benri carved bears out of special woods. The live baby bear, which served as his model, attracted the tourists who bought his cleverly carved wooden animals.

Tano, Benri's wife, spent her time copying ancient designs for decorating "attushes," the loose coats that were formerly worn by both Ainu men and women.

Toki and Haruko often spent their afternoons with their grandparents in the village. Haruko liked to join them in the dances which they performed for the sight-seeing tourists.

Stepping slowly behind the other dancers, they helped form the circle in the open space in the midst of the reed houses. Fuchi had taught Haruko how to move gracefully with her knees bent. The girl had also learned to make the shrill twittering cries of small birds which came from the lips of the older dancers. She clapped her hands in time to the songs they sang as they danced.

When the weather was good, buses and automobiles brought strangers to the model Ainu village. Visitors, old and young, came from the other Japanese islands. Now and then there were travelers from Europe, America, and other continents.

The strangers were welcomed in the reed houses. Ekashi pointed out for them the fire-holes where the Fire Goddess lived. He showed them the treasure corners with their shining Japanese lacquer boxes and bowls, and their curved warriors' swords.

Outdoors the visitors could stand by the log bear cage and watch its shaggy young prisoner sit up and wave its front paws in greeting. Toki often explained to them that this half-tame young animal would be the star of the village's famous festival for "Sending the Bear Back to Heaven."

"No tourists this afternoon! It is too windy. And I'm glad, Ekashi," Toki said to his grandfather on this cold autumn day. "You'll have time for more stories."

Some boys and girls on Hokkaido today are ashamed of their Ainu forefathers. They do not like to be thought different from their Japanese neighbors. But Toki and Haruko, with their grandfather's teaching, shared his pride in their past.

"Tell us more about A-e-oina, the Mighty Teacher, Ekashi," Haruko begged now. "How he came out of the Sky Country to show our ancestors how they should live on the earth! How he smuggled out the precious seeds for their planting, in spite of the tattle-tale dog."

There never seemed to be an end to their grandfather's tales. He remembered countless wonderful legends about the Ainu gods whom he called the "kamui."

Ekashi never seemed to tire of telling about Ainu Land in the olden times. And his grandchildren never seemed to be weary of listening to him.

A-E-OINA, THE DEMON,
AND THE TATTLE-TALE DOG

"I am A-e-oina, sometimes called O-ki-kirumi, favorite of the Great Kamui, the All-powerful God. Of all the smaller kamui whom he created, I was the most important." Again Ekashi was speaking as if he was the hero of the tale he was telling.

After the manner of the most famous Ainu tellers-of-tales, he was letting A-e-oina tell his own story. As was their custom, the Old Man was almost singing his words. It was as if he was reciting a poem, and he tapped out its rhythm with a small stick.

"The Great Kamui sent me, A-e-oina, down out of the sky to tell his earth people how they should live. That is why I am known as the Mighty Teacher.

"It was not easy to pass the tests which the Great Kamui gave me before I could depart on my mission. He had to make sure that I could stand hardship. So first he shut me up in a cave where it was dark and cold. Oh, it was so cold inside that cave that my fingers froze, like so many icicles. But I spoke not one single word of complaint. I did not even cry out, 'Oh, it is cold here.'

"Next I was thrown down close to the Kamui's fire-hole. So close was I that the flames singed my beard. They scorched my forehead. But I did not grumble. I did not even say, 'Oh, it is hot here.'

"The Great Kamui was pleased with me. He said,

'Now, go, A-e-oina.' So I gathered together the things I should need to teach the earth people how they should live.

"I took arrows for their hunting and spears for their fishing; digging sticks to open the ground for their plantings; and herbs to cure their aches and their pains. It was when I was gathering millet seeds for their eating that trouble came.

"Some of the smaller kamui were jealous of my importance. And so were God's heavenly creatures who walked on four legs. In those times, the gods and the heavenly animals both were important, one just as important as the other. And it was a dog who saw the millet grains which I had gathered up into my hands.

"'Stop! Stop! A-e-oina, stop!' that dog cried out. 'You shall not take those millet seeds away from our Sky Country. I shall warn all the other gods that you are stealing our precious seeds.' Like all the animals in the Beginning, that dog could speak with the words of the gods and of men.

"Well, before the tattle-tale beast could shout his warning, I hid my millet seeds in a pocket which I cut in the skin of my leg. The dog was just opening his mouth to summon the other kamui when I threw a handful of ashes into his open jaws. When he tried to give his warning, only a harsh barking sound came out of his throat. Since that day no dog has ever been able to speak with the words of the gods and of men."

As his grandfather paused, Toki said, "I remember, Ekashi, that's why we never give our dog cakes made of millet meal." The boy had heard this story before.

The Old Man nodded. Then he went on chanting his tale.

"When I, A-e-oina, had thus silenced the dog, I dropped down out of the sky. The Great Kamui made

12

*People
from the Sky
Ainu Tales
from
Northern
Japan*

a bright circle of light to shine round my head. The earth people saw me before I stood before them on the ground. They began to dance, and they sang, 'He comes out of the sky.' They clapped their hands. 'A teacher, sent by the Great-and-Important God, to tell us the secrets of his earth.' Somehow they knew this.

"The earth people listened well to my teaching. With sturdy reeds for their walls, and bundles of smaller reeds for their roofs they built comfortable houses. I showed the women how to weave cloth from fibers inside the bark of the elm tree. I taught them to cut their bark cloth and sew it together to make attushes, long coats that would cover their bodies.

"The millet seeds I planted for them grew well." Ekashi was now chanting this happy part of his tale with joy in his voice. "In wooden bowls the women ground the grain into meal, good meal from which they made soup and cakes for their daily food. Almost like magic was the way I showed them how to make the millet beer which they liked well to drink.

"Most important of all"—Ekashi's voice now was more serious—"I taught them how to please the kamui, the gods who live in the Sky Country, but who come down, now and then, to visit the earth.

"I told them that the open window in the east wall of each house should be the god's window. Through it the kamui could come and go as they pleased. Through it the hunters should pass the animals they brought home, so that their meat should be blessed. Bad luck, I warned them, would surely come to anyone who peeped in through a holy east window from outside a house.

"The Ainu never forgot their duty to the kamui while I, A-e-oina, ruled on the earth. When they ate and when they drank, they always remembered to give the gods a share. The small millet cakes they set out for them would grow bigger and bigger until they could feed many kamui. The drops of millet beer they let fall on the ground for the spirits would by magic fill many heavenly bowls.

"All these things I taught them. It was from me, A-e-oina, that men learned to make god-sticks, the white 'inau' with which they honor the spirits." The Old Man lifted up the willow wand he was whittling. It had a crown of curling shavings that hung from its tip. "The gods were pleased when they found such inau in their east windows. The kamui of the trees, of the millet patches, of the rivers and the ocean were happy when they were honored by gifts of these willow wands."

The new inau which Ekashi was making would be thrust into the edge of the fire-hole in the reed house. This would please Kamui Fuchi, the Goddess of Fire. Then she would continue to bless the house. Of all the hundreds of Ainu gods, Toki and Haruko, like Ekashi, loved this grandmother-goddess the best.

"Life was good under my rule," Ekashi went on with his whittling as he took up his tale again. "I, A-e-oina, gave the Ainu laws so that they might live together in peace, one village with another. The kamui often came to the earth in the form of animals, to give us their meat for our food and their skins for our clothing. The only thing they asked of us was that when they were killed, we should send their spirits back to the Sky Country with proper respect.

"With so many bear and deer on the land, there was plenty of meat. The river gods sent fish into the traps which I, the Mighty Teacher, taught our ancestors to make. Our millet grew well.

"But one day"—the Old Man's voice now had a frightening tone—"one day there came up from the dark underworld, a wicked demon god. He was bent on making mischief for the earth people.

"'Ainu Land shall be mine. Its people shall serve my pleasure instead of that of A-e-oina!' These were the words which the Evil One spoke to me, A-e-oina, whom the Great Kamui had set to rule over the Ainu.

14

*People
from the Sky
Ainu Tales
from
Northern
Japan*

"Well, I jumped upon the demon. With all my might, I pushed him down on the ground, but he bounded back again onto his feet.

"'I'll show you which of us has the most powerful magic, A-e-oina,' the demon shouted. 'We'll see which of us can light his pipe with greatest ease,' he cried.

"With a great leap into the air, he flew up and up until he could touch his pipe to the fire of the blazing sun. But before he returned, I, A-e-oina, merely laid my forefinger on the tobacco in my pipe's bowl. And lo, it was set afire.

"The demon was taken aback, but he would not admit defeat.

"'Let us see which of us can climb yonder mountain with greater speed,' he challenged. 'Watch, and you will see how quickly I shall reach its topmost peak.'

"Now I, A-e-oina had the blessing of the Great-and-Important God. So, as if they were pebbles, I rolled enormous boulders to block his way. I was already standing there on the mountain peak when he arrived. In every other contest which he proposed, I was the winner.

"'It is clear that I cannot get the best of the Mighty A-e-oina,' the evil spirit said to himself. 'But I still can make trouble for his people. If I cannot win in the daytime, perhaps I can at night when he sleeps.'

"So he waited until evening was near. Then he leaped up into the sky. And he followed the Sun

God when he disappeared in the west. He saw the spirit enter a cave, take off his robe of brightness, and lay himself down to rest.

"The demon then slipped quietly into the cave, and he took away the Sun God's fiery attush. Putting it on himself, he flew back to the sky. There he took his stand beside the Goddess of the Moon who was, as usual, sending her soft pale rays down on the sleeping earth people.

"At once the sky became bright as day, and the Ainu woke from their sleep. When they saw two moons in the sky, instead of one, they were afraid. And they turned to me, A-e-oina for help.

"I knew at once that the false moon was the wicked demon from the underworld. So I climbed up on the edge of a high cliff. There I pulled back the string of my golden bow. I aimed my silver arrow straight up at the false moon. It sped like the wind, and it did not miss its mark.

"The demon in the sky fell like a shooting star down onto the earth. Quickly I tore from his body the Sun God's attush of brightness. But before I restored it to its sleeping owner, I threw that wicked demon far out into the sea. By the magic of the Great Kamui, whose favorite I was, I turned him into a fish. And never again did our ancestors see two moons in their sky."

The children smiled at the happy ending of the story. Ekashi smiled too.

"All the Ainu were sad when I, A-e-oina, left them to return to the Sky Country. But they had learned their lessons well. They took care to please their gods, and throughout Ainu Land, all was well." Ekashi paused. Then he ended his tale by chanting, "So said the kamui. So said A-e-oina, the Mighty Teacher."

ANIMALS FROM HEAVEN

In the Beginning—so Ekashi told Toki and Haruko—the Great-and-Important God called on his smaller gods to help him in his task of making the world. There were hundreds of these spirits. In the Sky Country they had the forms of men and women. They lived up there just as people did down on the earth, so Ekashi said.

Some of the small kamui who came down out of the sky were never seen. Ekashi explained that they lived in the trees, in the rocks and the rivers, or inside the reed houses. Like Kamui Fuchi the Grandmother-Goddess of the fire-hole, the spirits who dwelt upon the roof beams and under the sleeping mats helped protect the household. But no one ever saw them.

Others such as the bear and the deer gods who came to serve the earth people, had the forms of animals and birds, or even fish. Ainu children like Toki and Haruko were always careful to treat all living things with care and respect. One could never be sure but that one of them might be a messenger from the Great-and-Important God.

"My grandfather told me many tales of how the animals from heaven helped the Great Kamui finish the world," Ekashi said. "I liked the story of the water wagtail, who was the very first bird. When the Maker-of-the-World was first setting the land down to float on the ocean, the wagtail stood beside him on the seashore. Its long tail beat upon the newly made ground, up and down, up and down. Without stopping, the busy bird smoothed out the rough shore so that one could walk upon it with ease. Look well at a wagtail my children, and you will see how its work was done."

Haruko and Toki nodded. They knew the slender black and white wagtail bird well. They were always amused when they watched its long tail, forever bobbing up and down. They liked its cheerful song as it moved so briskly about.

"There was another bird, however, who disobeyed the Great Kamui, and he was well punished." Ekashi shook his head. "This was the lark, the little bird which flies so low across the sky. As my grandfather told it, one morning the Great-and-Important God needed to send a message down to his earth people. So he called one of the smaller gods.

"'Put on the form of a bird,' he commanded. 'Go down to the earth as a little lark. Deliver my message and make sure you come back before the sun sets.'

"Straightaway that small god became a lark, and at once he flew off as the Great Kamui commanded.

"He found the earth to be beautiful. It was more beautiful even than the heavenly country from which he had come. So delightful indeed did he find the earth that the lark forgot God's command that he return the same day. Not until the next morning did he spread his wings and fly again into the sky.

"The lark had not risen very high above the tree-tops when he met the Great Kamui coming to look for him. He trembled with fear when he heard the angry voice of the Great One crying, 'O wicked lark! You have disobeyed my command.'

"'Your earth was so pleasant that I forgot that I should leave it the very same day.' So the lark tried to excuse his act of disobedience. 'I will gladly return now to the Sky Country,' he said humbly.

"But the Great-and-Important God replied to him in even angrier tones.

"'That you shall not do. Never again shall you fly up into the high heaven. Never shall your wings take you higher into the sky than you are at this moment.' This was the punishment which the Great Kamui set for the disobedient bird.

"The lark pleaded and pleaded for forgiveness. But there was no mercy for him.

"This story explains, Toki and Haruko, why today the lark never flies very high above the tall trees. Always we can hear him singing his begging song. That is why we call this little bird 'riko chiripo' or 'little bird that goes up into the sky and argues with God.'"

Another of Ekashi's stories was about a crow which once saved the sun, and it was a favorite of his grandchildren. The Old Man always stroked his beard lovingly as he recited it, for it was a tale which he himself liked.

"I speak of a demon god from the underworld," he said, "a wicked spirit who tried to spoil the Great Kamui's plans for his people on earth. One day as this Evil One felt the warm rays of the sun on his back, he said to himself, 'Without the light and the heat from the fiery God of the Heavens, men could not live. It will amuse me to take the sun out of their sky. I will open my jaws wide. I will swallow the sun. Never again will I let it shine down upon Ainu Land.'

"Now the Great Kamui heard the demon god's awful threat. Quickly he called upon one of his helpers. 'Put on the form of a crow,' he commanded. 'Fly into the highest heaven. The Evil One from the underworld means to swallow the sun. Somehow, good Crow, you must prevent this disaster.'

"The big black bird at once flew off to do the bidding of the Great Kamui.

The next morning the rosy dawn, so pleasant to see after the dark night, began to brighten the earth. The demon was waiting when the sun showed his face over the eastern hills. The crow arrived just in time to see the bright golden ball disappearing between the Evil One's jaws.

"The monster's great mouth was still open, and the crow flew inside it. With his sharp beak, he pecked at the demon's tongue. He pecked and he pecked until he forced the Wicked One to spit the sun out again into the sky. With his strong flapping wings the crow drove the spirit from the underworld out of the heavens and down over the edge of the earth.

"The crows in our millet patch know this story," Ekashi said. "That's why they dare to steal our grain. That's why they are so bold as to fly into our houses and peck food from our very eating bowls. They think this is their right, because of their ancestor's great service in saving the sun for mankind.

"No creature was ever more useful to the Maker-of-our-World than a certain fish," Ekashi continued. "This was a giant fish, almost as big as the earth itself. The Great Kamui chose the enormous creature to hold his earth steady as it floated on top of the ocean. That fish was so strong that its backbone could bear the weight, not only of our world, but of the six other worlds which lie below it."

Toki looked at his sister. Both children giggled. Their grandfather smiled too. He knew that this story did not agree with the geography lessons they learned in their modern Japanese school.

"Well, my grandfather believed the tale," he insisted. "He said that when that giant fish breathed, the ocean waters rose and fell. When the huge creature shook its mighty tail, the earth trembled. Houses

20

*People
from the Sky
Ainu Tales
from
Northern
Japan*

fell down. Rocks tumbled over the hillsides. My grand-father called it 'the earth-quaking fish.' "

A fox was the hero of another of Ekashi's stories about animals from heaven. This was the clever beast who helped the Good Gods get the better of the Bad Gods.

"In the beginning," the Old Man said, "the Good spirits and the Bad spirits were all mixed together in the Sky Country. It had not yet been decided which should have control of the world. Both wanted the power, and always they were arguing. At last they said they would hold a contest to settle the matter.

" 'We shall see which of us is quickest to announce the coming of the Sun God into the morning sky.' This was the test they agreed upon.

"The Good Gods chose the clever fox as their leader. He had already proved that he was smart by getting the best of the tiger. This happened when the two of them were matching their strength against one another. First they ran a race which was to take them from the very top of the world to the very bottom.

"The tiger bounded away on its much longer legs. But the clever fox took a firm hold on its tail. Like lightning the fox was pulled through the air. When the tiger arrived at the very bottom of the earth, the fox turned a somersault over the head of the panting beast. The slow-witted tiger did not know what had happened. But he had to agree that the race was a tie.

" 'Let us see which of us can roar the loudest.' It was the tiger himself who made this suggestion. And the fox agreed. He gave his sharpest barking cry.

" 'Did you hear me, Tiger?' he asked. And the tiger had to say 'Yes.'

"Then it was the tiger's turn. The sly fox thrust

its head into a hole in the ground. And the tiger roared. It was a mighty roar. But the fox, from inside his hole, cried, 'Roar louder, Tiger, I can hardly hear you.'

22

*People
from the Sky
Ainu Tales
from
Northern
Japan*

"The tiger was truly not very bright. He roared again with all his might. But again with his head deep in the hole, the fox shouted, 'You heard me well, Tiger, but I can hardly hear you. Try again.' Again and again the tiger roared. At last he roared so loud that he burst his lungs. And that's why there are no tigers in Ainu Land today." The Old Man laughed.

"So it was not strange that the Good Gods chose the fox as their leader in their final matching of wits with the Bad Gods. By agreement, the winners were to be those who spied the rosy light of the morning sun first. They should rule the world.

"The Bad Gods took their places on the plain facing the eastern sky. But the Good Gods, standing behind the fox, turned their backs on this place where the sun rises. Instead, at the command of their leader, they gazed up at the peaks of the mountains in the west.

"'Ho, ho! You look in the wrong direction,' the Bad Gods mocked their rivals. But the fox and his followers did not turn around. And it was the fox who first cried, 'We see the sun's light. There on the western peaks.' It was true. The western hills reflected the sun's brightness long before the fiery ball itself appeared in the eastern sky. This was lucky, for ever since they won the contest, there have been more Good Gods than Bad Gods upon the earth.

"We worship the Good Gods because they serve us well," Ekashi always tried to impress on his grandchildren how much the Ainu owed to the spirits. "They protect us from the Bad Gods, and they supply our food and our clothes. The Great Kamui sends them to the earth for our use. The fish in the waters give us good eating. The bear and the deer supply not only meat, but their skins to keep us warm. Of all the animals from heaven those two are our best friends. How should we not praise them?

"But we must never forget that in truth they are gods themselves." The Old Man's voice was firm. "Like the skylark, the beasts and the birds, also the fish, long to become gods again and fly back to the Sky Country. This they cannot do so long as they have on their earthly forms. When we kill them, we set their souls free and they can go back to heaven.

"So it is just and right that we take them for our use. To show our thanks, however, we should always send them off on their heavenly journey with proper respect."

"GOOD-BY,
DEAR LITTLE BEAR GOD"

"Dear little Bear God.
We have fed you.
We have petted you.
We have loved you as well
As if you were a child.

But the time has come now
For you to go from us.
Now you must return
To the land of the Gods.

Good-by, dear little Bear God,
Make a good journey.
Do not be angry that we must kill you
To set your spirit free."

Ekashi chanted these verses for his grandchildren one day in the autumn.

"This is the song I shall sing when the cameramen come to photograph the Bear Festival." The Old Man spoke quickly. He was excited that his village had been chosen for putting on, once again, the great Ainu celebration of sending the bear to the Sky Country.

It was a long time since a bear had been "sent away" properly on Hokkaido Island. The Japanese governors had forbidden it many years ago. They said the old Ainu custom of choking a bear to death was too cruel to be allowed.

Now, at last, a motion-picture producer was to

record the ancient festival for all the world to see. But this "Sending the Bear Away" would have to be just a game of "pretend." The bear would not suffer. It would not really die.

Toki and Haruko also were excited. They had never seen a Bear Festival. Not even their father could describe one for them. Only very old men and women like their grandparents could remember just how it had been done.

Ekashi, as chief of the model village had been called upon to advise the motion-picture director. He was to be the star of the production, and the village bear would be the hero of the plot. The children, themselves, would be in the crowd who would dance and sing in front of the cameras.

"A 'pretend' festival will not be as good as a real one," Ekashi said to Toki and Haruko. "Listen and I will tell you how we 'sent the bear away' when I was a boy.

"I remember one special bear in our village," he began. "It was more than fifty years ago, when I was eleven or twelve years old. But I have never forgotten how tiny that bear was when the hunters brought it in.

"My own grandfather was then the chief of our village. And he had sent the hunting party up into the mountains with this blessing.

'O, God of the Mountains!
Show these brave hunters many bear tracks.
Lead the dogs to the dens under the snow.

Spirits of the forest and the rivers!
Let them pass safely!

Kamui Fuchi, Mother God,
Keep them from harm!'

"My grandfather's prayers were answered. The dogs found a den, and the hunters killed the grown

bears to give us food. They brought home a wee baby bear for our festival. The tiny cub was crying, and my grandfather put it into the lap of my mother.

" 'Take the little Bear God,' he said to her. 'Feed it and comfort it so that it may live to grow fat and big.'

"It was truly a fine little bear, furry and soft. Its crying stopped as soon as my mother held it in her arms. Greedily it sucked millet paste off her forefinger. And when the night came, the bear cub snuggled comfortably beside her on her sleeping shelf. My mother soon came to love that little bear. So, too, did I.

"While it was small, I played with that little cub. I could wrestle with it at first, and often we rolled together on the ground. But as the months passed, the bear's hug grew rough. Its claws were sharp, and they scratched my arms. A nip from its teeth was no longer play. Soon it was too big to live with us inside our house.

"Then the men of the village set up a little log cage on low posts, just like the one we have here today in our model village. So our animal guest had a home all of its own. We treated our bear well. When we fed it, we petted it. And we praised it. Often I said to it, 'We love you, dear little Bear God.'

"Everyone knew the bear cub was being fattened for our festival. No one thought that sending its spirit back to the Sky Country was in any way wrong. It was our custom. My grandfather said the bear would be grateful. He said the little god would be tired of its life on the earth. It would long to return to its home with the other gods of the mountains. It was only right that it should die."

"When the bear's second year passed, it was the time. It had outgrown its log cage. Its body was fat, and its brown fur was glossy. So preparations for the festival began.

28

*People
from the Sky
Ainu Tales
from
Northern
Japan*

"The women began to grind more millet into flour for making cakes and dumplings. Fish had been dried for the soups for the feast. Tubs of millet, mixed with water and yeast, stood by the Gods' window, turning into beer that grew stronger each day.

"The men were busy too. They never stopped making fresh inau. Hundreds of these willow godsticks, with their crowns of curling white shavings would be needed. They would decorate our holy east window and the spirit fence outside it. Shavings would be stuffed into the skulls on the posts, left from former bear festivals. With the other boys, I gathered evergreen branches for the new festival post, which had been set up to receive the skull from our festival. And of course, fresh inau would be thrust into the fire-hole to honor Kamui Fuchi.

"The finest attushes were brought out. Everyone wanted to look his best. At other times during the year we did not often take off our clothes. We did not bother with baths. But for the Bear Festival, all the men and boys had their long hair trimmed. The backs of our necks, and our foreheads, too, were shaved. Old and young, men and women, boys and girls were washed clean all over.

"My grandfather had a new headband, I remember. It was made of neatly braided willow strips and a tiny carved wooden bear head was fastened into its front. A beautiful sword was brought out of the treasure corner, so that he might look like the great chief that he was.

My grandmother's cloth headband, also, was new. She wore her biggest beads and bangles. Great pewter hoops hung from her ears. She even rubbed fresh soot from the cooking pots into the tattooed markings on her face and her hands.

"Invitations were sent to neighboring villages." Ekashi remembered every detail. "My grandfather, as leader of the village, gave out this word, 'I am about to send our dear little Bear God back to his heavenly home. I invite you to the feast. Come to my house and help us do our bear honor.'

"The invited guests came, everyone dressed in his best. Some of them brought food and drink, for there were many to take part in the feast.

"When the time came for the bear to be led out of his cage, my mother hid herself inside our house. She could not forget how she had held it in her arms when it was a tiny cub. She wept when she thought how it must now be killed.

"I almost stayed inside with her, for there were tears in my own eyes. But a boy must be able to watch an animal die, so I took my place in the crowd around the bear's cage.

"My grandfather, of course, was host at the festival. He made a fine figure as he stood there in front of the crowd. With clear voice, he chanted the salute to the Bear God.

'Dear Bear,
You are good.
You have come to the earth
So that we may have food.
Your skin will warm our sleeping
In winter's cold.
We give you our thanks.

Now we will dance for you.
Now we will sing your praises.
Now we will lay down gifts for you
To take back to the sky.'

"The women brought bowls of food for the bear. Ornaments and swords from the treasure corner were laid before its cage. My grandfather lifted the little stick from across a drinking bowl and dipped it into the beer. The drops he let fall on the ground were for the bear and the other gods.

"When the bear was brought out of its cage, the dancing began. The animal looked stupidly at the circle of dancers, wagging its brown head this way and that. Just outside the God's window it was given a meal of dried fish which it gobbled up greedily. But the bowl of beer which was held close to its mouth was quickly sent to the ground with a blow of its paw.

"Then my grandfather chanted soothingly,

'Drink, dear little Bear.
Drink for your journey.
Today you will once more be a god.

We want you to be happy, dear Bear,
Oh, drink, dear Bear.'

"The bowl was held close a second time, but the bear only growled. It stood quite still, and this would not do. The honored guest of this feast must be as excited as those who were watching. It must be teased until its fierce spirit was roused.

"One young man jumped up on the beast's shaggy back and held fast to its ears. Everyone cheered and applauded his courage as the angry bear tried to throw him off.

"Then arrows began to fly from every direction. They had no sharp points but they pounded the sides of the bear like a torrent of rain. Even boys like me took part in the game. The bear grew more and more excited now, and the crowd shouted and howled.

"In even earlier times," Ekashi explained, "the festival bear was finally killed by being choked between two heavy logs. Many men put their weight on the top log and the animal's breath was squeezed out of its body.

*People
from the Sky
Ainu Tales
from
Northern
Japan*

"In the festivals I saw with my own eyes, the bear was treated more kindly," the Old Man continued. "We killed it swiftly so that it did not feel pain, with a thrust of a spear or the bite of an arrow. If logs were used for choking, this was done after it was already dead.

"My grandfather was a mighty man, and he had a mighty voice." Ekashi had greatly admired this Old Man. "It was fearful to hear him bark out the Ainu cry of triumph. 'Oh-ah-ah-ooo-o-o.' It ended with a shrill 'Oo-oo-ow-oo' like the howl of a wolf.

"When the bear was surely safe in the Sky Country, more gently he chanted a last farewell.

'Be safe, dear Bear!
And when you come back to this earth
As a newly born cub,
We'll give you welcome.'

"The bear was skinned with great care. Its meat was brought into the house through the holy east window. Every guest had a share of the feast. Even boys like me had a sip of the bear's warm blood so that we too should receive some of the animal's strength.

"When the guests were all gathered inside my grandfather's house, again he took charge. Before the lacquer cups of holy beer were passed round, the Old Man made prayers to the gods. Drops of the good drink were spilled into the fire-hole and my grandfather said, 'Oh, Kamui Fuchi, protect us. Join us in our feast and keep our dear little Bear God from harm on its journey.'

"What a feast it was! It lasted three days. We ate great piles of millet cakes. We emptied the beer tubs. For the young people there were games, tugs of war and wrestling matches. I remember I won the hoop game, with my spear going straight through it as it rolled along.

"Only when the last game was played and the last bit of food was eaten, did the festival guests go home. As for me, I went to sleep and, like everyone else, I did not wake up for a week.

"That is the way, Toki and Haruko, we sent the bear to the Sky Country when I was a boy. So truly, I say it was."

32

*People
from the Sky
Ainu Tales
from
Northern
Japan*

THE HUNGRY TIME

"There were hungry times as well as times of feasting in the old days in Ainu Land," Ekashi once explained to Toki and Haruko. "Usually our hunters could find a bear on the mountains. The deer came down the hillsides in such numbers that people had to put fences around their garden patches. Salmon and trout were thick in the rivers. Sometimes, truly, there were so many fish that the water splashed out over the land.

"Meat and fish were our main foods. Roots, nuts and vegetables, millet soup and cakes were used only as side dishes. And there was plenty to eat.

"But once there came a time when the bear and the deer, and even the fish disappeared from the earth." Ekashi stroked his beard to emphasize this dreadful thought. "It was an Old Man who first told me the story. Perhaps he was some kind of an earth god himself. Or he may have been just an ancient village chief like me. It was so long ago that no one now can be sure. But it does not matter. He told the tale, and I will tell it to you in his words."

"I, an Old Man, knew the gods were angry. They took the bear away from their dens. They hid the deer from our hunters. They sent the fish, and the seals, and the sea lions to the bottom of the ocean. They even dried up the millet and vegetables in our gardens. And we had nothing to eat.

"Yes, surely the gods were angry. But no one knew why.

"I, the Old Man, prayed to the god who protects the bear. I begged him to let them return to their dens in the mountains. I prayed to the god who has charge of the deer that they might come out of hiding. I even prayed at the river's mouth that the God of the fishes might call the salmon and trout out of the ocean and into our streams. I made fresh inau to honor every god I could think of. But they did not listen to my prayers.

"No deer tracks or bear tracks were seen in the forests. Even small animals which could be eaten— the rabbits, and squirrels, and raccoons—disappeared. There was not one fish to be caught, no salmon nor trout for our eating, not even sunfish to give us oil for our lamps. Our eating bowls were almost empty, and we sucked every drop of stew from their sides with our 'licking' forefingers. Oh, it was truly a hungry time.

"Why were the gods angry? That we had to find out. Only the Great-and-Important God, the Ruler-of-Heaven-and-Earth himself, could tell us the reason. So I sent word to the birds that I needed a messenger to fly to the Sky Country. 'I need a clever bird with strong wings who can fly into the highest heaven. I need a bird who can speak clearly and ask the Great Kamui to help us.'

"The first bird to make a polite noise at my door was a black crow. 'My wings are strong,' the crow said. 'I fly a straight course. And my voice can be heard. Let me take your message.'

"Now the black crow is one of the cleverest of birds. His 'caw' rings loud and clear. So I invited this visitor into my house, to a seat by my fire-hole. There I began to tell him just what he should say to the Great Kamui.

"'Tell the Great-and-Important God that his earth people are starving,' I began. 'Ask why the Bear God, the Deer God and the God of the Fishes are angry. Find out what we can do to bring back the bear and the deer out of their hiding places, and the fishes up from the bottom of the sea.'

"There was much else I had to say. But before I had really begun, that crow had fallen asleep by the fire-hole. I waked him with blows of a willow rod, and I drove him out of my house.

"The next bird to make a noise at my door was a blue jay. Like the crow, the handsome jay is a clever bird. His voice also is loud and clear. Surely the Great-and-Important God would hear the message he brought. So I invited him to sit with me by my fire-hole.

"I began to tell the blue jay what he should say when he reached the Sky Country. I gave him the words he should use in asking the Great Kamui about the Deer God, the Bear God and the God of the Fishes. But before I had half finished, he had tucked his head under his wing and was fast asleep. So I beat him with the willow rod and threw him out of my house.

"'Never will I find a wide-awake bird to carry my message to heaven!' I was just saying this to myself when there was a third polite noise at the door of my house. This came from a beautiful brown water ouzel. I liked this bird well and I bade him sit down by my fire.

"The water ouzel listened well while I told him of my mission. The more I spoke of our hunger, the wider awake he became. And when at last I had finished giving him his instructions, the good bird flew out through the east window and up into the sky.

"It's a long way to the sky home of the Great

Kamui. And it was not until three days later that the ouzel returned.

"'Have you found the Great-and-Important God? Did he tell you why the smaller gods are so angry?' I scarcely took time to welcome him back.

"'Yes, Old Man, I found the Great Kamui and I talked with the smaller gods. The Gods of the Deer and the Bear and the Fishes are angry because men are unkind to the animals they protect. When you kill them, you do not show them proper respect. How then can you hope that they will provide you with food?

"'Instead of killing them quickly with arrows, the hunters crush their heads with rough blows from heavy clubs. They tear off their skins without ceremony. They forget to do honor to the animals' spirits.

"'There is the same trouble with the fishes you catch. Fishermen do not take them neatly with harpoons and spears. Instead they beat them to death with sticks of rotten wood. For any fish spirit that is a sad disgrace. The God of the Fishes is rightfully angry.'

"'What then must we do?' I asked the water ouzel.

"'Bear skulls should be mounted high upon posts outside the god-window. Their jaws should be stuffed with fresh inau shavings. Fishermen should use harpoons and spears instead of rotten sticks. And there must be polite speeches to all the animal spirits. You must ask their pardon that they must be killed and go back to the sky.'

"I passed on this warning from the gods to my neighbors. And I said, 'We should make a feast for these kamui.'

"But in that hungry time, there was but little food and drink in our village with which to make such a feast. A handful of millet grains and a few drops of beer were all I could find.

"I gave the millet to my wife to pound into meal for cakes for the feast. As her mallet crushed the grain, surprisingly the meal rose to the top of her grinding bowl. It overflowed, not once but many times. Soon we had plenty of good meal.

"I poured out the few drops of beer, upon the bottoms of six drinking bowls. Before my very eyes, those six bowls were filled. So full were they that the little sticks laid across their tops danced up and down. Again and again I emptied them into our beer tubs until there was more than enough for the Gods' feast.

"We whittled fresh inau for all the gods. These willow sticks with their curling ornaments were set up through the forest, around the millet patches and along the banks of the rivers. Thus I made sure that all these smaller gods would be pleased. And I invited them to come to the feast.

'Oh, God of the Bear!
God of the Deer!
God of the Fishes
That swim in our waters.

Forgive us, we pray
For our carelessness.
Never again will we forget
To honor the creatures whom you protect.

Come to our feast, dear Gods.
Eat, drink and enjoy yourselves!'

"And the gods came! In through the holy east window of my house they floated. The Bear God, the Deer God, and the God of the Fishes. They ate and they drank. Like us men, the gods enjoy nothing so much as drinking good beer. They sang and they

danced all through my house, in and out the east window. Truly they enjoyed the feast we made for them.

"Suddenly, outside, a deer and a bear appeared. The Deer God and the Bear God pulled hair out of their hides. They blew these hairs far, far up toward the mountains. And at once large herds of deer came leaping down into our valley. A procession of fat bear came into sight.

"The River God called a huge salmon out of the ocean, and he lifted two shining scales off its back. These he threw far out into the water. At once our river was dark with swimming fish. Salmon and trout were there for our eating. Sunfish could now be had to give us oil for our lamps. Seals played with sea lions close to the shore. There was even a whale thrown up on the beach.

"The hungry time was over and we howled for joy. After that for many years there were always bear and deer in our land. There were fish too. But we were careful to kill the creatures with ceremony. We did not forget to share our food and our drink with the kamui. Always we put out a few drops of beer, a few millet cakes and a share of our meat.

"So said that Old Man of long ago. So he told the story." Thus Ekashi ended the tale of the Hungry Time in Ainu Land.

But Ekashi had more to say to Toki and Haruko. He wanted to explain why it was that there were so few hunters and fishermen in their country today.

"It was when the Japanese conquerors came that our bear and our deer again disappeared," he said. "Bullets from their guns destroyed the deer by the hundreds. The Japanese took the deer meat for making the meat called venison. Bear hide could be sold. Fish could be canned in the factories they set up.

"'Let the Ainu open the earth with their digging sticks,' they said. 'Let them grow more grain on their land. Let them plant rice such as we grow in the southern islands. Let their hunters and fishermen become farmers like our people there.'

"But rice does not like our northern cold." Ekashi shook his head. "Millet grows better here, and so we still use that grain for our cakes and to thicken our stews. Japanese rice wine, sake, is better than our millet beer, and those who have money can buy rice for eating and for making wine in Hokkaido stores."

Here Ekashi sighed as he stroked his beard. "Sometimes I long for the old days," he said. "I miss the exciting hunts on the mountains. I miss the taste of the strong meat of the bear and the deer."

YOSHI-TSUNI,
BRAVE WARRIOR FROM JAPAN

In Ainu Land, many tales are told about Yoshi-tsuni, the great warrior from Japan. But it was so long ago when he lived on this northern island that no one knows just who he was.

"Some people think he was the god, Okikirumi, or A-e-oina," Ekashi explained to Toki and Haruko. "They think so because like the god, he gave our people good laws, and he taught them better ways of living. Of course, it may be that he was a god, come down out of the Sky Country. But it is more likely that he sailed here from Japan when his jealous older brother drove him out of Honshu."

When this family talked about the hero, Yoshi-tsuni, the children's Japanese mother, Tano, always took part. She remembered the stories she had been told about him when she was a child. And this is the way she repeated them as they all sat around the fire-hole.

"Every Japanese boy and girl knows about Yoshi-tsuni," Tano said. "He is their favorite hero, and his life makes a fine story. Yoshi-tsuni and his brother, Yori-tomo, were the sons of a certain chief who died in a battle with the powerful Taira clan. Their sorrowful mother never ceased to tell them that they must punish the Taira who had killed their father. And Yoshi-tsuni remembered.

"When the boy was only seven years old, his

mother put him in charge of some good monks in the Buddhist temple near her home. She hoped that he, too, would become a priest. But the boy liked playing with his small wooden sword better than studying with the monks.

"'I will obey my mother,' the child said to himself. 'I will learn to be a brave warrior. Then I can fight the Taira who killed my dear father.'

"Every chance he got, the boy, Yoshi-tsuni, ran out into a clearing on the mountainside behind the temple. There he practiced and practiced with his small sword. Its wooden blade slashed the air, as he fought with the rocks and the bushes. His challenges to imaginary Tairas rang out fiercely.

"One afternoon there was a bright flash of lightning and thunder roared over his head. But no rain fell. Suddenly, Yoshi-tsuni saw a curious creature standing beside him. At first the boy thought it was only a bird, for it had wings and a sharp beak and there were claws on its feet. A second look told him that the beak was a long nose, and the pop eyes of the creature were those of a tiny man.

"'I am the King of the Tengu,' the wee creature spoke. 'My little people and I dwell in the woods on this mountainside. The Tengu are appointed by the Great Kamui to teach men about swords. We have watched you practicing here day after day, and we would like to help you to learn to be a great warrior.'

"The goblin king set the boy to fighting with his small subjects. Again and again they fought, and as the years passed, Yoshi-tsuni became so quick with his sword that he could defend himself against twenty of the lively mountain elves at one time.

"When the boy was fifteen years old, he had an even greater adventure. This was his meeting with a huge man called Benkei who was the terror of the

countryside. This Benkei, almost seven feet tall, was a collector of other men's swords. No enemy could defeat him in a battle. In his collection there were a full ninety-nine weapons he had taken from his brave opponents.

44

*People
from the Sky
Ainu Tales
from
Northern
Japan*

"At first Benkei paid no attention to Yoshi-tsuni. The lad was so much smaller, and the giant took him for a weakling. This annoyed Yoshi-tsuni, and he attacked. Somehow he managed to send Benkei's sword flying out of his hand. But the big man quickly recovered it.

Thanks to the teaching of his small friends, the Tengu, Yoshi-tsuni was able to keep out of the way of that sword in the giant's hand. Like a flea, he jumped this way and that way. Now he was in front of Benkei. Now he was behind him.

"Then, cleverly, the youth again knocked Benkei's sword out of his hand. As the big man bent to pick it up, Yoshi-tsuni tripped him so that he fell flat on the ground. The youth leaped up on his back, and he gave the victor's shout.

"Benkei admired the brave young Yoshi-tsuni. 'You shall be my master,' he cried, 'I will fight by your side.' And after that wherever Yoshi-tsuni went, there also went Benkei. With his help, this young Japanese hero won one victory after another over the Taira. They were well punished for killing his father.

"Now Yoshi-tsuni's older brother, Yori-tomo, had risen to power in Japan. He was a 'shogun,' the ruler of important lands under the Emperor. He was a vain man and he soon became jealous of Yoshi-tsuni's success over the Taira. When there was a new victory, Yori-tomo let the word go out that it was he, instead of Yoshi-tsuni who had fought the battle. He hounded his brother from one end of the land to the other. At last he ordered him to leave Honshu and never come back. Some say this caused Yoshi-tsuni to kill himself with his own sword."

So ended Tano's story of the Japanese hero. But Ekashi had more to say about him.

"Other people declare Yoshi-tsuni and Benkei escaped from Honshu in a boat," he said. "They sailed across the stormy sea to our island of Yezo. I, Ekashi, believe that this was what happened. Our ancestors tell how Yoshi-tsuni helped them in their battles with the Japanese invaders. They say he taught them many things beside hunting and fishing. He was truly a good friend of the Ainu. That is why there is a statue of him on the cliff that looks down on the Piratori River."

Toki and Haruko had once made a journey to see the hero's tiny temple there. His statue was really frightening. Clad in black lacquer-and-brass armor and with a curving sword in his hand, Yoshi-tsuni's statue stared out at them with popping eyes and a fierce grin.

"Tell us the story of Yoshi-tsuni's heavenly bride," Haruko begged. The Old Man smiled. This was his granddaughter's favorite tale of the Japanese hero.

"Well, once the brave warrior from Japan fell in love," Ekashi said. "He saw the girl only once when she stepped outside her father's house to admire God's beautiful world. She was lovely to look upon, and Yoshi-tsuni thought she was like a shining goddess from the Sky Country. He told all his friends that he must have her for his bride.

"But that beautiful Ainu girl would not marry the brave Japanese hero. When he heard from the marriage go-between that she said 'No' he fell into deep gloom. He could not sleep. He would not eat, no matter whether the food set before him was good or bad. His friends thought he would surely die of his love.

"'We must get help from the kamui,' they said. 'We must send a message to the Sky Country.' And they called on the water wagtail, the bird who was such a faithful message carrier.

46

*People
from the Sky
Ainu Tales
from
Northern
Japan*

"The good bird told the story to all the small gods. 'Yoshi-tsuni must be cured,' it said. 'He must sleep and he must eat and grow strong again so that he can help us to defend Ainu Land from invaders.' The little wagtail begged so hard that one of the goddesses took on the likeness of the Ainu girl. And she entered the house where Yoshi-tsuni lay on his sleeping shelf.

"When the hero heard her moving about, he peeked at her through the loose sleeve of his attush. To his joy, he saw a girl whom he took to be his beloved. He watched her straighten the mats on the floor about the fire-hole. He saw her fill the cooking kettle with fresh water. He gladly ate up the good stew which the goddess brought to his side.

"Yoshi-tsuni felt strength returning to his body. He was joyful and at peace now. And he went off to sleep.

"But the tale has a bad ending," Ekashi told the family. "When Yoshi-tsuni awoke, his beautiful bride was no longer there. Either it had been just a dream, or he had been tricked. But he was well again, and he had come to his senses. He decided to forget his lost love, and he went forth into the world just as before."

Ekashi thought for a moment as if he was searching his memory, and then he said, "There is another story about Yoshi-tsuni, but it is a tale that is hard to believe of such a brave hero. It does him no credit, for it tells of the theft of a treasure from his Ainu friends. It could perhaps have been another Japanese warrior, but the taletellers declare that it was he. The story goes like this:

"In time Yoshi-tsuni took for his wife a real Ainu girl, the daughter of a certain chief. For a long time he lived happily with her in the house of her father, and all was well. Then one day he refused to go out on the mountains to hunt with the chief, saying he did not feel well. And while the hunters were away he complained to his wife, 'I am not happy here. You do not love me, and your father does not trust me. Perhaps I should leave Ainu Land and go back to Honshu.'

" 'Do not say such bad words, Yoshi-tsuni,' his wife cried out. 'Why do you speak so?' She was almost in tears.

" 'I am told that your father possesses a book, an interesting ancient book, a very precious book. He keeps it hidden away, and I never have seen it. He has shown me his other treasures, his swords and his earrings and his beads. But never have I laid eyes on this book.'

"The chief's daughter thought for a moment and then she said, 'Yoshi-tsuni, you are my husband, a member of our family whom we love well. Surely it can do no harm to let you see our ancient book.'

"She brought out the treasure from its secret place, which Yoshi-tsuni marked well. The next day he went out as usual with the chief and the other hunters. But the following morning, he said again that he was not well and that he would stay at home. While his wife went to fetch water from the river, he took the book from the secret place. He packed it up with his other belongings, and he ran swiftly away.

"When his wife was inside the house once again, he jumped into his boat which was tied up on the shore. And he started off down the stream.

48

*People
from the Sky
Ainu Tales
from
Northern
Japan*

"As he was hunting in the forest, the chief had a feeling that something was wrong at home. He ran back like a deer, and he was just in time to see Yoshi-tsuni, in his boat, going down the river. The chief followed him, and his boat was the swifter. By the time Yoshi-tsuni had reached the river's mouth at the ocean, he had come close.

"Now the chief had two magic harpoons, a black one and a white one. And they would fly through the air far and far. First he threw the white harpoon, which caught in the side of Yoshi-tsuni's boat. The chief was about to pull it back, when the fleeing warrior cut its line. Then the black harpoon was thrown. Its sharp hook fell into the very middle of the boat. But again its line was cut, and the runaway was not caught.

"The chief shouted with all his might, 'Yoshi-tsuni, come back! Come back! Do not take away our precious book!' But the warrior did not come back. And that is why we Ainu do not have books of our own. That is why our language is not for writing or reading. We do not have our own words for either pen or ink."

Of course, Ekashi's story did not really explain why the Ainu have no writings of their own. But it did explain, for him at least, why the stories he told Toki and Haruko had never been written down by his ancestors. Instead they had to be handed down from one Ainu storyteller to another by word of mouth.

THE OLD MAN
ON THE MOUNTAIN

"You remember well, Ekashi," Toki said. "You do not need books to tell us stories out of the past."

That afternoon his grandfather had just finished a tale from the great Ainu poem, known as "The Yukara." Its name means "that which is told over and over," and it has been handed down in Ainu Land for many generations. In it there are exciting adventures of heros and warriors, and fabulous tales of powerful magic and mysterious gods.

"I must remember, my little bear," the village chief said, looking fondly at the boy. "Without books how should the ancient wisdom of our ancestors be preserved except that old people like me pass it on to young people like you. To remember well is a gift from the gods. It may be that, like the Old Man in the story, I received my gift from the heavenly ones when I climbed the tall mountain."

"What was that story, Ekashi?" Haruko spoke quickly. "Why did that Old Man climb the mountain?"

"Why does anyone go up into the high mountains, my little bird? The mountain gods call us, and we obey. Many is the time I have heard their voices in my mind. 'Come,' they say. 'Come now! Come into the hills!' And I would go.

"Of course that was in the days when I was young. Then my legs were strong enough to climb over

rocky hillsides. I could leap across mountain streams."
Ekashi sighed. "Now I am too old. Never again shall
I stand on the highest meadows and sniff the sharp
mountain air.

50

*People
from the Sky
Ainu Tales
from
Northern
Japan*

"The Old Man in the story also found the climbing
hard on the day when he answered the call of the
mountain spirits. Once out of his village, he started
along the steep path that led into the hills. He
climbed and he climbed. Sometimes thorn bushes
reached out and grabbed his ankles, and he had to
cut himself free with his hunting knife. Once a wicked
little whirlwind came directly down the path, blow-
ing leaves and dust up into his face. He jumped aside
just in time, and he spat with all his might at the
mischievous small demons that were making it turn
around and around.

"Now and again a young deer bounded through
the forest trees. But the Old Man did not run after
it. This day he had no thought of hunting. He was
intent on just answering the call of the mountain.

"Once a bear came straight at him. But he knew
what to do. Of all the gods on the mountain none
is more powerful than the god of a big tree. So the
Old Man ran for protection to a tall elm. He threw
his arms round its trunk. He pressed his body against
its bark so that the bear should not see him.

" 'Save me, Spirit of this Elm,' he cried out. 'Do
not let the sharp claws of this bear tear my flesh.'
And he was saved. As if by magic, the bear turned
around and went off down the path.

"Another time, the Old Man came to a mountain
stream, and he said a prayer to the god who lived
in its rushing waters. 'I salute you, Water Spirit,' he
cried. 'Help me to pass safely. The mountain is calling
me.'

"Up, up, and up he went." Now there was envy

in Ekashi's voice. "His old legs were weary. But he did not turn back.

"The people of his village were worried when the Old Man did not come home at the sunset. The next day at dawn they followed his footprints along the trail up the steep slope.

"One of the searchers found the Old Man's bow and arrows at the foot of a tree. Another spied his food bag lying under a bush. So they could be sure he had gone that way.

"'The Old Man could not have climbed farther,' they said at last. 'The mountain from here on is far too rugged. No doubt a bear has carried him off.' They sadly turned around and went back to their village.

"But that Old Man had gone on. With his hunting knife he had carved a strong hook out of a forked branch. He had used this to pull himself from tree to tree, ever climbing upward toward the sky. As if by a miracle, he had finally reached the very top of the mountain.

"Oh, the air was good there on that mountaintop. Clear and cool! The afternoon sun shone down on the carpet of green grass in the little clearing. And the Old Man laid himself down to rest in the shelter of a young tree. Sleep came at once. He slept and he slept. He never remembered how long.

"It was the sound of singing that wakened him, loud merry singing! Through half-opened eyes he looked upon a strange sight. The moon was bright in the sky and dancing there on that mountain meadow was a company of gods from the Sky Country of the Great Kamui. Many there were, leaping and dancing, and greatly enjoying themselves.

"'These are no ordinary men and women,' the Old Man decided. 'Spirits they surely are, come down from heaven to visit the earth.' And what if they

should be angry with me that I have spied upon them? His fear made him pretend that he was still asleep.

"But the playful gods and goddesses were filled with their own happiness and enjoyment there on the mountaintop. They prodded him gently and their leader said, 'Wake up, Old Man! You shall have a gift to reward you for your climb. You shall choose for yourself. Would you like to have a truly beautiful face, a "shipi-rika-konrushi?" Or would you prefer to have an ugly face, a "shiuinhe-konrushi?"' Their words tumbled out on the air like a flock of butterflies.

"The Old Man was confused. Of course he would rather have a beautiful face. But he could not twist his tongue properly to make the correct sounds. What came from his lips was quite another word—'shui-kuruka-konrushi,' which is to say, 'I want to speak well.'

"'Shui-kuruka-konrushi!   Shui-kuruka-konrushi!' The gods all shouted the word at the same time, and they danced to its rhythm.

"The Old Man felt his tongue loosen. Words rolled out of his mouth like the flowing waters of a hillside brook.

"When he made his way down the mountain to his village again, his family and his friends made him a fine feast of welcome. They had feared he was lost.

"At once they noticed the difference in the Old Man's speaking. When he told of his adventure with the dancing gods, his words were like the music of a poem. The guests at the feast listened to him with delight.

"From near and far people came to his house. They crowded about his fire-hole, and they begged him for stories from the Yukara. Not until nearly dawn would they allow him to go to his sleeping shelf.

"The Old Man was able to tell one story after another because the gods had given him also the gift of remembering. Like beads on a string the tales came. And his verses were as smooth as the songs of the mountain gods on their lofty playground.

"All through Ainu Land that Old Man was known as 'yukara-kuru' or the 'Yukara-Man.' "

54

*People
from the Sky
Ainu Tales
from
Northern
Japan*

THE FROG'S TATTOO

One day Toki brought a live frog from a nearby pond to show his grandmother. No matter how busy she was, the Old Woman always had time to listen to him and examine the treasures he had found outside the village.

"Look at this frog's feet, Fuchi," Toki cried. "It has tattoo marks like yours on its feet."

The Old Woman raised her eyes from the straw mat she was weaving. She put it aside so that she could examine the fingerlike claws on the front feet of the frog.

She nodded her head and she called out to Haruko, "Come, see! There are marks here which are truly like those tattooed on my hands."

"Your frog's tattoo proves that the old story about the wicked ancestress of the frog could have happened." Fuchi smiled. "It shows that long, long ago she could well have been an Ainu woman whom the Great-and-Important God punished because she disobeyed his rules. Sit here beside me and I'll tell you how it was." She took up her weaving again, and as her fingers moved among the strands of straw, she told them this tale.

"It happened when the earth was very new. Then all the women in Ainu Land had tattoo marks on their arms and their hands and their faces."

Haruko looked up at her grandmother. The blue-black tattoo marks which followed the curves of the Old Woman's lips made it seem as if she always was

smiling. The tattooed lines on her arms ran straight and true. Neither Haruko's Japanese mother, nor her Japanese schoolteacher, nor indeed any of the younger Ainu women she knew had such marks.

"When I was a child," Fuchi continued, "Ainu women still had their mouths and their arms tattooed. The Japanese rulers of Ainu Land had said that tattooing must stop. But our people did not give up the custom easily. 'The Gods will be angry,' they protested.

"In the Sky Country all the goddesses are tattooed," the Ainu grandmother continued. "Kamui Fuchi herself gave us our tattoos. When she first came down to earth her own mouth, her arms and her hands were beautifully marked. She taught the women of the earth how to make their skins ready with lotion made from the bark of certain trees. She showed them how to prick patterns into their skins with the sharp points of hard stone.

"Into the tiny pricked places, they learned to rub blue-black soot which they collected from under their cooking pots. When the pricks healed the color was fixed so deep in their skin that it could be seen as long as they lived."

Fuchi's tattoo was faded now that she was so old. But it still marked her mouth. It still made the patterns of lines on her arms and her hands.

" 'Begin to tattoo your girl children when they are small.' That is what Kamui Fuchi said. 'Prick a small pattern each year. Then it will not hurt too much. When they are grown up the tattoo will be complete. Then the world will know that they are ready to marry.'

"Tattoo marks are helpful, so Kamui Fuchi taught us," the Old Woman continued. "They made Ainu women look like the tattooed goddesses of the Sky Country who are protected by the Great Kamui.

Demons seeking to enter their bodies to make them ill were frightened away by their tattooed mouths. So said the Goddess of Fire, Kamui Fuchi, the sister of the great A-e-oina."

The children's grandmother paused. Then she remembered another reason why the Ainu women of early times liked to be tattooed.

"Women without tattooing were not welcomed at the village feasts," she said. "When they died, people believed they would not be allowed to enter the pleasant afterworld of the gods. They would go instead to the dark realm of the demons. There the wicked ones would pounce upon them. With sharp knives they would tattoo their mouths and their arms all in one day. You can guess how painful that would be."

"But tell us about my frog, Fuchi." Toki was growing impatient at all this talk of women and tattooing. Everyone knew that long ago girls had to be tattooed. "What did the ancestress of the frog do that made the Great Kamui angry?"

"She did not obey." The Old Woman's voice was stern. "She did not obey her parents when she was small. She did not obey her husband when she was grown. She did not obey the Great Kamui's good laws."

Toki and Haruko had been taught from their earliest years how great a sin it was to disobey. They knew fabulous tales of naughty children who did not do as they were told. They were careful themselves to obey older people lest they be sent to live with the disobedient boy who ended up on the moon.

"The ancestress of your frog, Toki, was good in the beginning. But somehow a demon must have taken possession of her. For she refused to fetch water for her mother's cooking pot. She would not help with the weaving and sewing the attushes for the family. At last in her wickedness, she bewitched her poor parents so that they died.

"The girl had no trouble in finding a husband, for her tattoo was beautiful. But she would not obey him as a wife should. She would not cook his food, and she would not mend his clothes. At last he fell dead because of her evil magic.

"A second husband met the same fate. There was a third one, and a fourth. Six husbands she had in all. And all six of them died. Truly she must have been possessed of a demon.

"Well, the Great-and-Important God in the Sky Country sees all and knows all that happens on earth. And he was angry at the wicked deeds of this woman. As often before, he sent a bird to carry his message to her.

"'The Great Kamui is angry,' the bird told her. 'He says you are not fit to live among the good people of the earth. So he is turning you into a frog. Woman, henceforth you shall have a frog's body. And you shall live in the mud of the marshes and bogs.

"'Your children shall be slimy creatures like you, and men shall despise them. You shall have to leap high into the air to catch the insects and flies which are to be your food. With contempt, people will call you "Old Jump and Eat."'

"Before the bird had finished speaking, the woman felt a chill spread through her body. Her legs and her arms began to shrink. At last they were no bigger than those of a huge frog. The only thing that reminded her that she had been a woman were the lines of her tattoos of her front feet.

"In shame, that frog-woman hopped away to hide herself in the marshy edge of the nearest pond. You can know she was unhappy. And her children and grandchildren were unhappy too. Each spring, when the frogs come back from the southern island of Honshu, you can hear them complaining, 'ker-chunk, ker-chunk.' Oh yes, the ancestress of the frogs was well punished by the Great Kamui. So says the old tale. So it says truly."

Fuchi was silent as she wove the straw reeds together. And then she said, "There is another one of God's creatures who wears a tattoo mark. This is the sparrow. If you will look closely you will see the dark spot on its beak.

"It happened when the Maker-of-all-Things had just finished creating the world. He had put the beasts on the land, the fish in the water and the birds in the air. His great work was done and he was about to go back to his Sky Country again.

"'We shall make a fine farewell feast for the Great Kamui,' the creatures decided. They busied themselves with preparations for the food and the drink. All helped except the small sparrow. She was so busy tattooing her beak that she thought of nothing else. She did not hear about the feast until it was almost too late.

"'Come, Sparrow, come to the feast!' the other creatures called to her. Her work of tattooing was only half finished, but, of course, she rushed off to join in the festivities. That is why the sparrow has that one little dark spot on the upper part of her beak. She never got around to finishing her tattoo."

THE MAD DANCERS
OF UPO-POU-SHI

"Beware of Pauchi Kamui, my children," the old Ainu grandfather often warned Toki and Haruko about this naughty goddess. "Take care that Pauchi does not lead you into trouble as she once did the people of Upo-pou-shi."

The children knew what a troublemaker this kamui was. Often they heard Ekashi pray to Kamui Fuchi when he put newly whittled inau beside her fire-hole, "Oh, Good Mother-Goddess, Kamui Fuchi," he would say. "Use your power to keep Pauchi Kamui far away from this house. Prevent that mischief-maker from bringing sickness in through our god-window. Keep her from causing accidents to our hunters."

Ekashi thought that the kind Kamui Fuchi had power over the other small gods.

"In the Sky Country," the Old Man explained, "Pauchi Kamui was known as 'a good goddess.' She was the Heavenly Weaver who made beautiful garments for the other gods. No earth-woman could weave such fine cloth out of the fibers of the elm bark. No human fingers could embroider such gay patterns on sashes and headbands. Yes, in the Country of the Gods, Pauchi Kamui was praised.

"But on earth it was different. Different, indeed!" Ekashi shook his head. "Like many another kamui, Pauchi liked to drop down out of the clouds and visit the Great Kamui's beautiful world. Once arrived in Ainu Land, she straightaway began to play her tricks.

"There is a certain village which men call 'Pauchi-Kara-Kotan. This is to say 'Pauchi-made-village.' It lies in a deep gorge in the midst of the mountains. Nowhere on Hokkaido are there so many rocks. All tumbled together. Big rocks and little rocks. Smooth rocks and jagged rocks. Rocks shaped like bears, and rocks shaped like birds. Only a mischievous god like Pauchi Kamui would have so stirred up the earth.

"It's an unlucky man or woman or child whom Pauchi Kamui chooses to tease," Ekashi continued. "Once her spirit finds its way into the body of an Ainu, no one knows what may happen. She can make him behave as he never would if he was in his right mind.

"I once had a neighbor in my grandfather's village whom this wicked goddess drove completely out of her wits. This was Ochin, who was just about to marry a fine young man. He was a good boatman and he could swim like a fish. Surely it was Pauchi Kamui who caused him to drown in the river. Surely, too, it was Pauchi who took control of the mind of the poor weeping Ochin. For Ochin was a good girl. She knew well our rules of modest behavior. Never in her right mind would she have thrown off her attush before all the village and begun to leap about in a wild dance. At the top of her voice she sang

'I am a bird,
I can fly
High as the sky!

Over the river
Over the mountain.
I am a kamui.' *

* Adapted from "The Bear Worshippers of Yezo," Edward Greey, 1884.

64

*People
from the Sky
Ainu Tales
from
Northern
Japan*

"The girl capered and jumped about. She flapped her arms as if she was truly a bird, and she cawed like a crow. At last she bounded away up the hillside, and she disappeared into the deep woods. Never again was that poor girl seen in the village.

"I was a bold dancer myself when I was a young man." Ekashi had his "remembering look" in his eyes. "But our Ainu dances are calm. We move round and round, and though we bend and we sway while we sing our dance songs, we do not lose our heads.

"It was bad enough that Pauchi Kamui drove poor Ochin mad when her lover had drowned. But it was much worse when she threw a whole village into a frenzy. That happened more than three hundred years ago at a spot which later became known as Upopou-shi, or 'The Place of Dancing and Singing.' No one has ever told me what it was that started the people there to dance with such fury. But suddenly, every man and woman, every boy and girl, was jumping about. They bowed and they leaped. They barked our ancient Ainu cry like so many mad dogs. Indeed they were mad themselves.

"Now our ancestors were modest, just as we are today. So we can be sure it was Pauchi Kamui who was the cause of this dreadful happening. For women as well as men threw off their attushes. They had no shame at all at being seen in their undergarments. They thought of nothing else but their wild dancing.

"Hunters did not hunt. Fishermen did not fish. Women took no thought for their cooking pots. They left their babies alone in their cradles. And they gave no food to the old people.

"My own grandfather told me this tale. He said many of the mad dancers dropped dead. Others, like the girl Ochin, danced away up into the mountains. Still others stopped suddenly and were turned into birds that flew up into the air with flapping wings.

"That was a sure sign that it was Pauchi Kamui who drove the people of Upo-pou-shi into their wild dance. For it is told that when this wicked Goddess of Mischief was first put into the world, she appeared in the midst of a cloud of black birds.

"So my own grandfather said it was," Ekashi declared. "And he told me other tales of dancing people with almost no coverings on their bodies.

"Pauchi Kamui herself once appeared as the heroine of the story. This was one time when the good in her nature could be seen. It was once when she brought with her good luck instead of bad luck. With her dancing she saved the people of a certain village from a band of wicked robbers.

"It happened one evening, and the band of evil men were floating down the river toward this village.

" 'Look! There on that rock!' One of the robbers pointed to a young woman dancing in the dim light of the dusk. She was without her attush, and she was beautiful.

" 'Oh! Oh! Whoever saw such a sight?' The robbers stared at the thinly clad dancing girl. Their eyes were fixed upon her and they did not notice where their boat was taking them. Not until it was too late did they see the rushing rapids ahead. They were swept over a great waterfall to their death on the sharp rocks below it.

"Those who told the story were sure that the dancer was Pauchi Kamui herself. She knew what she was doing. She wanted to destroy the evil men before they could harm the people of that village.

"So they said it was. So it could have been."

Toki and Haruko thought they could hear doubt in the tone of Ekashi's voice. But the Old Man never told them just how much of his wonder tales he himself believed.

THE ONE-EYED MONSTER

The mosquitoes were thick. The gnats flew in clouds around the heads of the two children as they picked berries in the forest. They brushed them away with cries of annoyance.

"Why did the Great Kamui put these pests in the world?" Haruko complained to her grandfather.

"Oh, it was not the Great-and-Important God who was to blame, my child," the Old Man replied. "It was a demon god, a wicked demon who wanted to torment the earth people. It happened like this." He sat down on a fallen log, and the children came close.

"Like the good gods in the Sky Country," Ekashi began the story, "demons from the underworld liked to visit God's earth. But they came for no good purpose.

"Once a certain very bad spirit took on the form of a monster for his appearance in Ainu Land. Children saw it first, and they were almost breathless with fright.

" 'The monster was as tall as a man. But it was not a man,' they said. 'It was hairy all over, just like a bear. But it was not a bear although it had claws and great teeth. No, it was neither a man nor a bear. And it had one enormous eye, set in the center of its forehead.'

"No one believed the children's tale until the hunters themselves began to meet the one-eyed mon-

ster in the forest. 'The creature is truly fearful to look at,' they reported. 'Its one eye is as big as a man's hand, with his fingers spread wide. And it burns bright as fire. We have tried to shoot the monster, but it was as if our arrows had no sharp points. They bounced off the creature's body and fell useless on the ground.'

68

*People
from the Sky
Ainu Tales
from
Northern
Japan*

"The hunters said that the monster ate up every living thing it could find. They found the bones, not only of deer and bear, but also foxes and wolves. The men themselves had terrifying narrow escapes.

"Each night when the village dogs barked, the Ainu trembled on their sleeping shelves. The dogs drove the monster away, and for a time they were safe. But their meat and their fish, drying on racks outside their houses, were gone in the morning. One unlucky man who followed the monster up the mountainside was never seen again in that village.

"'Until that one-eyed monster is destroyed we will not go forth to hunt,' the Ainu decided.

"But their wives begged them for meat. 'Our children are hungry,' the women wept. Something had to be done.

"The Old Man of that village at last went to one young hunter named Oto, who was noted for his bravery and for his skill with the bow. 'I will go up the trail,' Oto consented. 'I will try to find at least one deer to feed the little ones. But I will go only as far as the edge of the forest.'

"In truth, even this brave young man trembled at the thought that he might meet the monster. But he said to himself, 'I will pray to the tree gods, and it may be they will send me a deer out of the deep woods. It may be they will have pity on our hungry children.'

"As he went up the trail, Oto's steps were uncertain. His eyes were forever turning this way and that, following each tiny rustling in the bushes. Before he realized where he was, he had followed a deer far into the woods.

"Suddenly there was a stirring in a thicket at one side of his path. The deer had bounded away, but some animal was surely there. The young hunter, slowly and fearfully, crept nearer the sound. His heart was chilled when he saw the furry head of the monster amid the leaves. The demon's one fiery eye was staring straight at him, and he did not know what to do. He was afraid to run, for surely the monster could outrun him. Now he needed every bit of courage he could find in his heart.

" 'My arrows will not pierce his tough hide.' Oto knew this from the tales of the other hunters. 'But an eye is soft,' he said, 'soft as a jellyfish. Perhaps my arrow can enter his body through his eye.'

"The creature had not moved. Its burning eye remained fixed upon the hunter. Oto took careful aim, and his arrow sped to its mark. It carried its poison deep into the monster's great eye. And the fearsome creature fell dead.

" 'This monster was surely a demon,' the young hunter said to himself. 'What if its strong magic should bring it to life again? To prevent that I will burn its body to ashes.'

"Oto gathered dry leaves and small sticks, and he laid them up all around the beast's hairy body. Soon a hot fire was blazing about it as it lay there on the ground.

"Oto put on more and more wood. He kept the flames going until the demon's coarse hair and tough flesh, even its great bones, were burned up. All that was left of that fierce one-eyed monster was a pile of gray ashes.

" 'I had best scatter these ashes far and wide on the wind. Then even this demon's magic cannot put them together.' Oto said these words to himself. And he added aloud, 'Now, Demon, you can never make mischief for our people again.'

"But that young hunter did not know the power of demons like this one. He did not guess that it would still find a way to torment God's people on this earth.

"As the ashes from its burning floated slowly about on the breeze each tiny gray bit became a mosquito, a gnat or a stinging fly.

"So it was that these insect pests came into the world." Ekashi rose from his seat on the log. He shook his bushy head and he added, "But it is far better to be annoyed by a mosquito or gnat, or even a horsefly, than to be carried off to be eaten up by a fierce monster with only one eye."

The Old Man smiled. The children smiled too, which showed they agreed with him.

FOX MAGIC

One afternoon, Ekashi was putting newly shaved willowcurls between the jaws of a fox's skull. This was to be mounted on a wooden post in the god-fence outside the sacred east window of the model house. Toki and Haruko were watching.

"A fox's skull looks odd in the midst of bear skulls," Toki said to his grandfather. "It's so much smaller."

"And the spirit that lives in a bear's skull is good, while the fox spirit can be very, very bad." Haruko too sounded doubtful.

"Both of you speak the truth," Ekashi said then. "A fox is smaller than a bear, but his magic is big. And not all foxes are really bad. My grandfather always said it was better to do honor to gods like the fox kamui even if they were only half good. When I was a boy, we always had a fox's skull on our sacred shelf near the east window. We thought this would please the fox kamui. It might keep them from playing their tricks upon us."

The Old Man stroked his beard.

"There is a story about two fox brothers, I remember. One was bad. One was good. I'll let the good fox tell you the tale."

"My brother and I were different. I, the good fox, am speaking. He was big and he was strong. As for me I was small and I was weak. He was always playing mean tricks and fooling men while I liked humans who were good to us. Sometimes I even tried to do them a good turn.

"One day my wicked brother said, 'Ho, Puny One, the Ainu of the house at the bend of the river has gone away. He makes a long journey across the wide water to trade in Japan. He has taken his deer skins and his bear skins to exchange for sake and rice, and perhaps some good cloth. So his wife sits alone in their house, with no one to protect her.

" 'What does that matter to us?' I, the good fox, asked my brother, the bad fox.

" 'It will be easy for me to change my form into that of an Ainu,' he replied, 'I shall visit her house. I shall steal her soul away, and she will be in my power.'

"Oh, my brother was truly bad. It is a dreadful thing to take away a person's soul. Now, I had a good heart, and the woman's husband had done me no harm. 'That Ainu does not trap foxes,' I objected. 'Why should you play such a mean trick on his wife?' But my brother would not give up his plan. So, though I was weaker and younger than he, I determined to try and keep the poor woman from losing her soul.

"By my own magic I took on the form of a man. And I went to her house at the bend of the river.

" 'I come to warn you of danger,' I said to the Ainu's wife. 'There will come here, seeking shelter, a fox spirit who has changed himself into an Ainu. Beware, Woman, beware! For he is truly a fox, and he comes to steal your soul out of your body.'

"That woman would not believe me. She declared firmly that such a thing could not happen.

" 'Well, then look, and you will see for yourself,' I told her. 'This is what you must do. Boil together some fish roe and seaweed and give it to your visitor for his supper. Watch carefully when he has eaten

and he begins to pick the sticky fish eggs from between his teeth.'

"The Ainu's wife agreed. She knew well that no one can eat fish roe and seaweed without removing the tiny eggs from between his teeth.

"The Ainu's wife agreed. And it happened just as I said it would. The stranger, my bad brother, in the form of an Ainu, cleared his throat politely at the door of her house. And she invited him to come in. We sat down, the three of us, by the fire-hole, eating our supper of fish roe and seaweed. When the meal was over, I took up a little knife, and delicately, I picked the fish eggs from between my teeth. I, too, was playing the part of an Ainu.

"But my brother forgot to be so careful. He lifted up his attush and used the sharp claws on one of his hind feet to scrape the eggs out. One could see clearly that he was not a man, but a fox."

Ekashi shook his head as he went on with the story, speaking always as the good fox.

"The woman did not seem to notice, however. She gave us our places on the sleeping mats, and soon she and my brother were snoring happily. As for me I did not close my eyes. First I wrapped up a few caked ashes and cinders in a bit of cloth and I laid the small packet gently in the opening of the woman's attush.

"At midnight I saw my bad brother rise from his mat. He seized the packet of cinders from the woman's attush and he ran out of the house. He thought he had taken the poor woman's soul!

"I followed him and I took a shorter way home. When he arrived I was lying on my own sleeping mat beside our fire-hole.

"I could not help laughing when he unwrapped

the little packet to examine the stolen soul. He barked in fury when he saw that it was only a cinder cake.

"'You helped that woman,' he accused me. And at first I was afraid of his anger. But my own magic was strong enough to protect me.

"When the woman's husband came home at last from his trip to Honshu, he brought with him bags of rice, tubs of sake and rolls of fine cloth. But he had hardly put these treasures away before his wife told him about her soul's narrow escape. You see, I had told her how I, the good fox, had saved her from my brother, the bad fox.

"'This kind fox saved my soul,' she explained. 'But for his magic you would not have found your wife alive to cook your supper tonight.'

"'Praise and thanks be to you, O Fox Kamui!' He spoke to me at the east window. 'I will make you many inau. When you go to the Sky Country, your skull shall have a place of honor on our god shelf.'

"And so it was. While I still was on earth, I grew fat on that Ainu's offerings of fish. I soon became as big and strong as my brother. And I guarded that Ainu's house so that that wicked fox should never return.

"So said the good fox spirit in the old tale."

PAN'AMBE AND PEN'AMBE

"How is it that the fox spirits have such strong magic, Ekashi?" Toki asked his grandfather.

"The foxes are the descendants of a demon who lived down over the edge of the world," the Old Man explained. "Their magic comes from that ancestor, and only the power of the Great Kamui and his favorite, A-e-oina, is greater.

"Once in the days when the world was new, A-e-oina and that demon had a great fight. First the demon threw the good kamui into a blazing fire. He thought he had destroyed him, but at once A-e-oina was standing before him, untouched by the flames.

"Next it was A-e-oina who pushed the demon into the fire. Not only once! Not only twice! But so many times did he throw him in, that the Evil One's body was completely burned up. As he tried to rise out of the flames, the demon blew his ashes upward in a great swirl of smoke. Somehow A-e-oina knew that the demon would try to join them together again. So he, the powerful god, blew the ashes down, and he scattered them far and wide over the ground.

"With his strong magic, then the demon turned those ashes into foxes. Black foxes and red foxes ran everywhere over the land.

"So it is that the foxes are really small demons, with a demon's magic. Some are smarter than the others, however. Listen to the old story of Pan'ambe and Pen'ambe. Those two foxes were neighbors, and

Pen'ambe was often jealous of Pan'ambe because he seemed to have better luck.

"Well, one day Pan'ambe was standing on the bank of the river, looking across to the opposite bank. There he could see the castle of the Japanese lord, Matsumae, who ruled Ainu Land. The fox's mouth watered when he thought of the rich treasures that castle must hold.

" 'I wonder what would happen if I could make my tail stretch across the river and into a window of Lord Matsumae's castle.' He spoke aloud, and the words were hardly out of his mouth than his tail began to stiffen. It grew long and thin. Longer and longer! Thinner and thinner! Stiffer and stiffer! Soon it was as firm as a strong wooden rod, and its end came to rest on the sill of one of the windows of the castle.

"The Lord Matsumae saw the strange happening, and he marveled. 'Surely this is a gift from the gods, I can hang my best garments upon this rod to air.' And he called to his servants, 'Bring out my silk kimonos. Put my gold embroidered sashes upon it. The sun will be good for them.'

"It was done, and the great lord went away to attend to affairs of state. The servants were busy with their other tasks. Pan'ambe by his magic power, could see that no one was watching.

"Gently, gently, he drew his bewitched tail back across the river. He pulled it without harm to the fine garments attached to it.

"It was a rich prize his tail brought him." Ekashi nodded. "Pan'ambe sold the silk kimonos and the gold embroidered sashes for a great deal of money. Now, in his house, there was always sake to drink and fine white rice to eat.

"All the fox neighbors envied Pan'ambe. They

marveled that he should have become so rich. Especially Pen'ambe was curious.

"'Tell me, Pan'ambe,' he said, 'tell me how it is that last year you were poor like me and this year you are rich?'

"When Pan'ambe told how he had tricked the Lord Matsumae, his jealous neighbor exclaimed, 'Truly that was good magic. I'll try the trick myself.'

"Now Pen'ambe's fox magic also was strong. He had no trouble at all in stretching his own tail across the river to the house of the Lord Matsumae. He set its tip securely on the same window sill, and the Japanese governor cried out, 'Another gift from the gods!'

"'We shall put out my kimonos and sashes again,' he said to his servants. That Japanese lord was so rich that there was no end to his possessions. 'But we must be more watchful this time so that they shall not disappear.'

"Pen'ambe rejoiced when he saw the silken kimonos and the gold embroidered sashes hanging on his own bewitched tail. They would make him just as rich as his neighbor, Pan'ambe.

"But his greed was great. He did not wait to make sure that no one in the castle was watching. The last sash was hardly laid upon his tail, before he began to draw it away from the window. Lord Matsumae himself, saw his kimonos moving toward the river.

"'A thief steals my treasures,' he cried out. 'Stop him! Cut the clothes pole before they disappear.'

"His servants were quick enough to catch hold of the fox's tail before it had gone far. With sharp swords they cut through it, and the Japanese lord's treasures were saved.

"Poor Pen'ambe! He had no rich garments to sell.

He was as poor as before. And only a part of his tail came back across the river to him. The greedy fox hid himself inside his house, and it was a long time before he came out into the world again. Who would not be ashamed to be seen with only half a tail? Pen'ambe knew well that his neighbor, Pan'ambe and the other foxes would laugh at him."

THE BATS OF RU-PE-SHI-PE

Toki was excited. He had found a dead bat on his way home from school.

"I shall use this bat's head and skin to make me a little charm," he told his sister Haruko. "I shall dry them and wrap them in willow shavings left from Ekashi's inau. I shall keep my charm always in my pocket. It will give me the wisdom of a bat, and I will learn faster in school."

Haruko laughed. She shook her head and she said, "You talk like Ekashi himself. How can you be sure that your charm will have magic?"

"Well, I'll ask our grandfather," Toki insisted. "He'll say that it does no harm to take heed of the things our ancestors believed."

Haruko looked at the dead bat with distaste. But she went along with her brother to find the Old Man in the Ainu village.

The children's father, always busy with his wood-carving, and their mother, at work designing a new attush, only smiled when they saw the little dead "flying mouse." They did not perhaps have much belief in such charms. But it was different with Ekashi.

"I'll help you skin your precious 'mouse-bird,'" he said to the boy. "We'll put its head and its furry skin in the east window to cure. Then I'll shave you some special inau curls for wrapping it up."

As the Old Man examined the small brown creature he said, "This is a fine bat, Toki, my little bear.

Surely it will bring you good luck. Who can say that it will not help you learn faster at school?

"Everyone knows that a bat is very wise and very brave. How else should the Earth Kamui, Poyaumbe, have chosen a bat to guard his castle when he went to fight the Demon of Smallpox in the underworld. That is a good tale. And a bat would tell it like this."

"Once the Kamui Poyaumbe became greatly annoyed with the demon of the Dreadful Sickness of Smallpox. Again and again people died in the villages which the Great-and-Important God had put in his keeping. Again and again those villagers heard the 'zing' of his smallpox arrows, bringing the Dreadful Sickness into their homes.

"'I will go find this demon, and I will put him to death,'" Poyaumbe said. 'I will not fight him here on our beautiful earth. Instead I will seek him out in his own kingdom over the edge of the world. But first I must find a wise and brave guard to watch over my castle.

"'He chose me, the bat,'" Ekashi was making the animal the teller of the tale. "Poyaumbe said to me, 'Bat, you are wise. Bat, you are brave. None other can better watch over my people while I am gone.'

"Poyaumbe then went off to the underworld. All was well at his castle until one day there appeared the Demon of Smallpox himself. While Poyaumbe was seeking him in the underworld, he was walking about here on the earth.

"'Ho, Bat, you must be brave and wise,' that demon said to me. 'Or Poyaumbe would not have put you in charge of his castle. But I am wiser and braver. We shall prove this in a battle.'

"We fought. I beat him about his face with my wings. But he shot one of his arrows into my heart. I fell to the ground. My bones were weak as water.

The demon rejoiced, for he thought I would die. But the Great Kamui, looking down from the sky, raised me to my feet. I seized the demon's own poisoned arrow and I used it against him. This time he was himself shot in his wicked heart. He fell dead on the ground. And the Great Kamui did not bring him to life again. At least not just then.'

"After all, all men knew that we bats are both wise and brave. Otherwise, how could we always get the best of the Demon of Dreadful Sickness?"

Ekashi told Toki and Haruko that there was small-pox in Ainu Land often in the days of his ancestors. That was long before men found out how to vaccinate themselves against its attacks. Whole villages were destroyed by the "arrows" of the demon.

"He often came in a boat, that Demon of Dreadful Sickness," Ekashi was remembering other tales he had been told when he was a boy. "He moored his boat on the seashore or in a river. Or it floated down out of the sky and was tied up by a rope of cloud on a mountaintop.

"In the spring hundreds of little birds with red and white heads announced his arrival in Ainu Land. Bad luck came to the foolish person who harmed one of these little messengers. The Dreadful Sickness was sure to find its way into that person's home." Toki and Haruko knew this story. They were careful never to throw even a tiny pebble at the small red-headed birds.

When Toki's bat's skin and head were cleaned, they were put in the east window to dry.

"May the charm bring you good marks at school," the Old Man told the boy. "May it keep you safe from the smallpox demon, as the bats of Ru-pe-shi-pe kept the people of Niwan safe in the old story."

"How was that, Ekashi?" Haruko asked. She had

been watching and listening as her grandfather and her brother made the charm ready.

"One day in early spring," the Old Man began, "the little red-headed birds came in great flocks to the village of Niwan. When the sun went down and the sky grew dark, the people said they could hear the snap of the bowstring of the smallpox demon. The sound was close, and they ran out of their village to find some place to hide.

"As their refuge they chose the damp marshes near the Springs of Ru-pe-shi-pe. The night was cold, and they huddled about a bright fire which they built on the edge of the marsh.

"The Ekashi of Niwan feared that the Demon of Dreadful Sickness would find them there in the light of the fire. But without its warmth, they would have died of the cold.

"The 'zing' of the demon's arrows were very near now. 'He comes. Oh, he comes,' they cried out to each other. 'And he surely will find us.'

"But just then there came another sound, which drowned out the snapping of the demon's bowstring. This was the noise made by hundreds upon hundreds of bat's wings. They had seen the bright light of the fire and they flew straight to the cold marshes of Ru-pe-shi-pe.

"Those little mouse-birds flew in circles around the leaping flames. Around and around! It may well be that it was because they loved the bright light. Or the Great Kamui may have sent them especially to save the people of Niwan. Bats, bats, and more bats flitted around those villagers. So many of the flying creatures there were that they formed a thick curtain. The people and their fire were completely hidden from view.

"The awful voice of the smallpox demon came out of the darkness.

"'Where did they go? Those people of Niwan, running away from me! Where are they now? I look and I look. But I cannot find them.'

"Disgusted, the Demon of Dreadful Sickness went back to his boat and sailed away. So it was that the village of Niwan was saved by the bats of Ru-pe-shi-pe."

THE GOLDEN MARE

Of all the journeys which Toki and Haruko made with their grandfather, the one they enjoyed most was to the big Hokkaido horse farm.

"Our land has long been famous for its horses," the Old Man told the children. "When I was a boy, horses, like the deer and the bear, could be found on our mountains. They were wild, and yet they were easy to tame. Those wild horses were small, and they were sure-footed on the rough mountain paths. They wore no shoes but their horny hoofs were hard.

"Men went up into the hills in the early dawn to drive the wild horses down to their villages. Some they sold in the horse markets. Others they tamed and used themselves to carry their bundles of deer hides and bearskins to the Japanese traders who came to the shores of Ainu Land.

"I, myself, often rode a young horse which had only just learned to carry a rider. It was good to gallop over the land in the morning sunshine."

"Where did the wild horses on the mountains come from, Ekashi?" Toki asked.

"Who can say where they came from?" his grandfather answered. "Perhaps they were brought here on early trading ships from other countries. Perhaps the traders left them behind when they went away again. Or it may just have been that they were descended from the 'Golden Mare,' as some people

"Setta-Yuk, a hunter, came home from the moun-
used to say. This is how that ancient tale is told.
tain one day to find his house empty. A pot of stew

was bubbling in the cooking pot over the fire. But his wife was not there.

"'Katkimat (the woman who does the work of my house) may have gone out to work in our millet patch,' he thought, 'I'll just go and find her there.'

"But she was not in the millet patch.

"'She may be dipping water up from the river. I will look for her on its bank.'

"But she was not on that river bank.

"'Well, then,' Setta-Yuk said to himself, 'she is surely out on the mountainside, gathering firewood.' With this thought in his mind he climbed the path that led into the woods beyond his village. But no trace of his katkimat could he find.

"Something surely was wrong. His good wife worked hard. She kept their house well. She tended the garden. She wove mats for the floor. She cooked his food. Oh, he must find her at once.

"Perhaps the neighbors had seen her.

"At the door of the reed house next his own, he coughed politely. Then he cleared his throat 'Eh! Eh! Eh! Um-m-m-!' So he warned his neighbor that he was there. And when he was invited to come in, he rubbed the palms of his hands gently together and stroked his beard in salutation.

"'Have you seen my good wife?' he asked. 'My house is empty. A pot boils over my fire-hole. But my katkimat is not there. She is not down by the river. She is not out in my millet patch. She is not gathering wood. I thought it might be that she was paying a visit to your wife.'

"But his neighbor shook his head. 'No,' he said to Setta-Yuk. 'She is not here.'

"It was the same at the next house, and at every house in the village. No one had seen the lost wife of Setta-Yuk. It was as if she had fallen off the edge of the world.

88

*People
from the Sky
Ainu Tales
from
Northern
Japan*

" 'Surely it is the work of some demon,' Setta-Yuk said as he stopped to rest in the shade of an ancient oak tree. Being a wise man, he was always careful to honor the spirits, and before he sat down he faced the tree trunk and he bowed.

" 'Oh, thou divine God of this Oak Tree,' he cried out, 'I bow low before thee. Thou, whom the Great Kamui set upon earth fully grown, thou art wise. I call upon thee for help. My good wife, my katkimat of many years, has disappeared. She is not in my house. She is not down by the river, not in the millet patch, not in the forest. Tell me where I can find her, O Spirit of this tree. And I will make many inau to set up all around your trunk.'

"Setta-Yuk bowed again. And he thought he heard a voice floating down to him out of the leafy crown of the oak.

" 'I shall be pleased to have inau,' said the Tree Spirit. 'And gladly will I help you. Go around to the other side of my trunk. There you will find a fine golden mare. She will carry you safely up the path through the clouds to the Sky Country. There, in the shining city of the Great-and-Important God, you must ride through the streets and sing out your sad story. Some of the gods may know what you must do to find your katkimat.'

"Setta-Yuk was overjoyed when he saw the fine golden mare. In no time at all he had galloped up through the clouds into the highest heavens. As the Spirit of the Oak Tree had directed, he sang as he rode through the shining streets of the glorious city. At the top of his voice, so that all might hear, he sang this song—

'Oh, Divine Gods,
Divine Goddesses, too
Hear the sad story I have to tell.

People
from the Sky
Ainu Tales
from
Northern
Japan

My wife has been taken
Out of my house,

Where can I find her?
Tell me, I pray.'

"Over and over he sang his dismal song. Up one shining street. Then down another. He sang and he sang.

"At first the divine people of the Sky Country were amused by the man on the Golden Mare, riding around and singing his song. But in time they grew weary because of the noise he made and they asked the Great Kamui to send Setta-Yuk back to the earth.

" 'Ride your golden mare back to the Oak Tree,' said the Great-and-Important God. 'The Tree Spirit can now tell you where your wife can be found.'

"Setta-Yuk lost no time in galloping down through the clouds to the earth. Once there he bowed low before the ancient oak.

"Again the voice came out of the topmost branches of the tree. 'It was a demon who carried your wife away,' the spirit said. 'That evil one shut her up inside a big box in the land of the demons that lies under this earth. But while you were riding on the golden mare around and around the Heavenly City, he watched you. His eyes never left the sky, and he listened to your song. He still is peering up into the clouds to see where you have gone. If you make haste, you can set your wife free before he knows what is happening.'

"So Setta-Yuk galloped his golden mare over the edge of the world and down to the lower realm of the demons. There, to his joy he found his lost wife and he put her up behind him on the mare's back. Together, with the blessing of the Great Kamui, they reached their home safely.

"Setta-Yuk kept his promise to the Oak Tree. The inau he set into the ground about its roots were many. And the Ainu never forgot to put fresh ones out when the old ones were knocked down by the force of a storm.

"The happy Ainu gave a great feast to celebrate his success in finding his wife. His guests ate and drank, and they admired the golden mare.

"'She is a gift to me from the Spirit of the Oak,' Setta-Yuk told them. 'I shall see to it that she is well cared for. In time she will give birth to many colts. And they will be the ancestors of all the horses in Ainu Land.'

"So the Spirit of the Oak Tree told the Ainu it would be. And so it was."

THE FLYING SWORD

A sword that flew through the air by its own magic is the hero of this story. Perhaps it was the same kind of curved Japanese sword which hung in the treasure corner of Ekashi's model Ainu house. The tale does not say. But one difference there surely was—the magic sword had a blade of shining steel. Its edge was so sharp that it could cut through a tall pile of hard metal coins.

"Why are the swords in this treasure corner without blades?" Toki asked his grandfather one day when he and his sister were helping the Old Man rearrange the treasures against the north wall of the reed house. Under his direction the children were putting the shining black and red lacquer boxes and bowls back into their accustomed places.

Haruko straightened the folds of the ancient embroidered coats that hung against the wall mats. She liked best of all the Ainu treasures, the necklaces of huge beads with their great round metal ornaments, and the elaborate metal earrings.

For Toki, the most exciting treasures were "the shining ones"—the ancient swords without blades, in their handsome carved cases. His grandfather stopped their work long enough to hang a fine embroidered sword sash around the boy's neck. Toki felt very important as he looked down at the glossy black sword case at his side.

"Why do these swords have no blades?" the Old Man repeated the boy's question. "It comes from long ago when the Japanese came to our island, then known as Yezo. Our forefathers soon found that they came not just to visit but to conquer Ainu Land. So they fought them with all their might, trying to send them back to their own island. They gladly traded their deer hides and their bearskins for the swords and the daggers of these smooth-faced men from the south.

"The Japanese swords had sharp steel blades. Their daggers had points that could bite deep into a man's body. They were far better weapons than their own Ainu hunting arrows and fishing spears. So when our ancestors got hold of the swords of their invaders, they turned them upon their enemies.

"Our forefathers were brave, Toki. But they were greatly outnumbered. Little by little, the Japanese conquered the island of Yezo. And one of their first acts was to forbid Ainu men to own swords with blades.

"But even though they have no blades, we Ainu have treasured our forefathers' swords." Ekashi stroked his beard. "Their sheaths were handsomely carved. Some were inlaid with gleaming metal. To remember how they once looked, Ainu carvers made blades of wood. But these had to be hidden up under the roofs of their houses, lest they too be taken away.

"The old swords had magic," Ekashi said. "Some had magic so strong that a warrior had only to point one at an enemy and he fell dead. Another old tale says that a mere rattling sound like that of a sword would frighten a robber away.

"There was once an old woman who was left alone in a fort when the men went forth to hunt. A band of robbers came to attack that fort and they were at its very door. Inside they heard the sound of rattling metal.

"'That could be the fort's magic sword,' the robbers said to each other. They remembered stories they had heard of this terrible weapon there which ate men by the hundreds.

94

*People
from the Sky
Ainu Tales
from
Northern
Japan*

"'There must be a giant inside this fort,' one of the robbers declared. 'No other could shake the mighty sword so hard.'

"But in truth the sound did not come from a sword. The clever old woman had found an ancient rusty ax. It was loose in its handle, and when she shook it, it did sound like a sword. She shook it and she shook it, and the robbers, in terror, ran away from the fort.

"But the best magic of all was that of the sword which flew through the air, all by itself." Ekashi remembered this tale as they were finishing their work in the treasure corner. "That sword's power was great, even greater than that of the demon which it destroyed. It happened in this way." The Old Man went over to sit down by the fire-hole, and the children followed.

"The demon was wicked as most demons are. He liked to torment the people of a certain village, and from his home on a cliff nearby, he often came to their homes. He stole the bear meat which the hunters brought down from the mountain. He tore down the racks upon which the women were drying fish for the winter eating. He even led children away into the deep woods. It was three days before one lost boy was found.

"'We must get rid of that demon up there on the cliff,' the village people said to each other. They made many inau for Kamui Fuchi, and they prayed to her at their fire-holes.

"'Dear Mother Goddess,' they said. 'Keeper of our homes and protector of our families! We need your help badly. The demon on the cliff will surely destroy

us. Send us a sign. Tell us what we must do to rid our village of this Evil One.'

"That very night, the chief of the village had a dream. In it Kamui Fuchi came to him and she said, 'Ekashi, in the village at the second bend in the river there is a sword which has powerful magic. Borrow it, and send it forth with your bravest young warrior. With its help he will be able to destroy your tormentor.'

"The Old Man of that village went himself to ask for the loan of the magic sword. Everyone said that the bravest young warrior of them all was one whose name was Shongo. So the magic sword was put into Shongo's hands and he went off to find the demon on the cliff.

"The Wicked One's cliff was high and steep. Again and again Shongo tried to climb its rocky side, but he could not find even one little foothold. And he could see that the demon was waiting for him on the cliff's rocky edge.

"The demon laughed when Shongo tried to build a footbridge of reeds from a nearby rock. With his evil magic he pulled the Ainu's bridge apart before he could finish it. Shongo saw then that there was no way for him to get close enough to fight hand to hand with this enemy.

"'It is too far for me to thrust my sword into his body,' Shongo decided. 'It may be too far also for me to throw my sword. But I will try.'

"Shongo took a deep breath. With all his might he flung the magic sword into the air. The villagers who had gathered to watch, gasped with wonder. For that shining sword flew up toward the demon like a darting bird. It traveled by its own power, and it did not stop until it had pierced the heart of the demon on the cliff.

"One can know that Kamui Fuchi was helping the

brave young Shongo. For the magic sword left behind
it a trail of her own bright red fire.

"So the story was told in the long ago," Ekashi declared. "So said the ancient tellers-of-tales."

The
Flying
Sword

TWO TERRIBLE FISH

Ekashi knew stories about two terrible fish, and Toki and Haruko liked them very much. One tale ran like this:

A long time ago there was no island at all in a certain lake on the island of Hokkaido. And where its low marshes are now there was then a high mountain.

There were many fish in that lake, fish that were good to eat. When the lake was not frozen, fishermen went out every day to throw out their nets. Usually they brought home plenty of trout for their cooking pots.

One day a young fisherman was just drawing in his full net, when out of the water ahead of him there rose the head of a giant fish. It was a frightening sight. That fish was almost as big as a whale. Its nose came out of the water in the shadow of the high mountain peak at one end of the lake. Its back fin made a dark line all the way to the other end. There its giant's tail lashed the water in the mouth of a river.

The young fisherman had never seen such a thing. Fear filled his heart when the terrible fish dived straight at his boat. Of course it upset and he was thrown out into the lake. Before he could swim to safety on shore, the monster's great jaws opened wide and he was swallowed up.

The other fishermen out on the lake that day at once turned their boats around and made for the shore. They told the horrible tale, and the next day not one man in their village was brave enough to take his boat out on the lake.

A few days passed. The giant fish did not appear. People said that it must have been just a dream. Such a thing could not have happened. So a few fishermen decided to try throwing out their nets once again.

But once more the terrible fish rose to the surface of the lake. Another fishing boat was upset. Another young fisherman disappeared between the jaws of the monster.

"What shall we do?" the women of that fishing village asked one another. "If our men cannot fish, how shall we eat?" In their part of Ainu Land bear and deer were seldom seen. Fish gave them their food.

"I will pray to the Goddess of Rivers and Lakes," their Ekashi said. "Perhaps she will help us."

So they made many inau. Willow wands with their curled crowns of freshly cut shavings were like patches of white snow on the banks of the lake.

"Oh, Divine Kamui! Call away this terrible fish, that we may have food." The Old Man of the village cried out to the unseen protector of the lake. The people brought bowls of sake and they poured many drops upon the shore to please her. But it was as if the kamui had not heard them.

The very next day the monstrous fish lifted its head out of the water at the foot of the mountain. Its tail beat the water into foam at the other end at the river's mouth. And no fisherman, young or old, was brave enough to go forth in his little boat.

There was soon hunger in the village houses. The fish which had been dried for the winter was soon eaten up. Hunters came home empty-handed from the forest. Almost no food was left.

Now there was, in that part of Ainu Land, a young

fisherman named Usu, who was known for his courage. He came to the Ekashi, and he said, "Old Man, I, Usu, will kill that terrible fish. I will throw my harpoon. It will fly true and it will bite deep. I will save our village from starving."

The villagers gathered on the banks of the lake, and all the men prayed to the kamui to keep Usu safe. The young man went bravely out alone in his boat. He waited and waited near the place where the monster fish usually raised its head out of the water. His harpoon, with its sharp-pointed hook, was held high and ready.

At last the monster appeared. Its head was just halfway up above the water. Only one eye could be seen. Usu's harpoon was thrown like a hunting spear. It found its way, deep and true, into that fish's eye.

The angry monster swam wildly about. It dived and it leaped but it could not dislodge the barbed hook. It tried to upset the young fisherman's boat, but with the harpoon in its eye it could not see very well.

How fiercely they fought! The monster fish and the young Ainu! The creature pulled on the harpoon's line with all its might. Usu also pulled and his little boat spun around and around. Somehow the quick-thinking fisherman managed to throw his harpoon line up and around the mountain peak which rose above that part of the lake. There must have been magic in the air. No doubt the Goddess of the Lake was helping.

Usu thought he had won the fight. But the monster fish was strong. It gave a great jump and it jerked on the line with all its weight. So mighty was that pull that the mountain peak was toppled right into the lake. By good luck, or by the help of the gods, it fell on that monster fish, and buried it deep in the bottom of the lake.

"One can know that this happened," Ekashi always said when he told the tale, "because men who live on that lake, point to the island made by the mountain's top rising out of the water. They also show visitors the marshy hollow where the mountain formerly stood."

The other "terrible fish" was a whale. It was a great whale which often swam close to the shores of Ainu Land. Like the giant fish in the first of Ekashi's stories, this whale too swallowed fishermen, one after another.

Now the Great-and-Important God saw what was happening and he was angry with the whale.

By a water wagtail he sent a message to the God of the Low Places in the Ocean.

"Take your sharp sword," he commanded that god. "Go out and kill that wicked whale which is devouring my earth people who fish."

Now the God of the Low Places was not very smart. He went down to the seashore and he called out to the whale, "Monster, the Great Kamui is angry with you. He commands that you depart from this shore. He demands that you cease to torment his people who fish here."

But of course, words had no effect upon that monster of the sea. As before, he continued to swallow every fisherman who took his boat out from its mooring.

"Use your sword. Cut the monster in two." This was the next message which came from the Great-and-Important God in the Sky Country.

The smaller god was so excited that he completely forgot that he was wearing his own sword. He ran thither and yon, trying to find some other small god who would lend him a sword with which to cut the whale in two.

"Lend me your sword," he would say, "so that I may carry out the command of the Great Kamui."

But those he met only smiled at his stupidity. Why did he want theirs, when his own sword was hanging at his side? They only laughed. They did not take the trouble to tell him that he already had a sword.

At last the God of the Low Places came to the God of the village of Tobetsu. There, on the seashore, again he cried out, "Lend me your sword so that I may cut the whale in two." That village kamui laughed more loudly than all the others.

"Why don't you use your own sword?" he cried. "Why don't you fight the whale with the sword that hangs by your side?"

Then the God of the Low Places truly was ashamed. To make up for his foolishness, he determined that somehow he would kill the sea monster.

"If you will not heed the command of the Great Kamui," he shouted to the whale, "you will have to bow to the force of his magic strength.

"Help me, Great-and-Important God." The smaller god shouted up into the sky. "Put strength in my arm!" And the Great Kamui must have heard him. For his sword flashed through the air. It slashed the whale in two, and the fishing people were saved.

In Tobetsu, the Ainu used to point to Whale Mountain there. They said it is really one half of the monster whale. The other half no doubt fell away, down and down, upon the ocean bottom.

THE "LITTLE PEOPLE"

"They were small. Very small! Only a few inches tall. And they lived in holes in the ground. That's why they were called the 'Koropok Guru' or the 'persons who dwell below.'"

Ekashi was telling Toki and Haruko about the strange little people who, he said, lived long ago in Ainu Land.

"My grandfather called them the 'earth spiders,'" the Old Man explained. "He did not know just how small they were. He said some people thought they were two or three feet tall. Others declared they were much smaller, only a few inches in height." Ekashi smiled. "It's hard to imagine men and women so tiny that several could find shelter from a storm under one burdock leaf.

"The old taletellers told that the fishing boats of these tiny men, were made of the thin leaves of bamboo grass, sewed tightly together. When they caught a herring, it took the men in five of their fishing crews to pull it in to the shore. All the men in their village helped them kill the fish with their tiny clubs. If they were truly that small, they must have been some kind of gods." The old man shook his head doubtfully.

"It is more likely, I think," he said, "that these 'little people' were dwarfs, perhaps three feet in height. But even so, it is hard to believe the strange tales that are told about them. One story describes how the Koropok Guru once captured a whale. The

sea giant, no doubt, was washed up on a beach not far from their village.

"It must have been a strange sight to see the tiny men swarming over the whale's head, beating it to death with their small clubs. It must have taken them years to eat up the whale meat which they cut into strips and dried in the sun there on the edge of the ocean. But then"—Ekashi nodded—"the bear could have come down from the mountains to help.

"The Koropok Guru were big enough and strong enough to dig homes in the ground where they could keep warm in winter. Their pits were only about three feet deep, and they were roofed over with domes made of wood, bark and earth. I myself have seen pits which are said to have been left by the Little People. Some of our own ancestors also lived in caves in the hillsides. They, too, had underground shelters from wintry weather. But these caves were different."

"I do not think I should have liked grown men and women who were so much smaller than I am." Haruko was trying to imagine what the Koropok Guru were like.

"Our ancestors did not like them either," Ekashi said. "And the Koropok Guru did not like their much bigger Ainu neighbors.

"Such tiny people must be demons, the Ainu said. Such big people can only be wicked giants, the little dwarfs thought. So there was war between the two."

Ekashi told the children about the small forts built by the Koropok Guru. The piles of stones found inside them, he thought, could have been used as weapons to drive their Ainu enemies away. Little moats, muddy ditches about three feet deep, surrounded their strongholds. But these hardly seemed enough to keep full-sized attackers away.

"The Koropok Guru fought with all their might to protect their pit homes." Ekashi seemed to have sympathy for the Little People. "But the Ainu were determined to rid their land of these 'earth spiders.' They stuffed dried grass in the smoke-holes in their roofs and they set it on fire. Smoke filled the pit dwellings, and, like real spiders, the Little People came running out of the ground. Their men were killed. Their women and children were made into slaves by the Ainu victors.

"In time the Little People were all destroyed. Many were taken down to the river or the ocean where they were drowned.

"There is a story that when the last Koropok Guru chief was thrown into the water, he put a curse on his enemies.

"'You shall never forget us,' the little man shouted before he disappeared from sight. 'Our curse never shall go away. No longer will you enjoy eating the tender skins of the fish you pull out of the water. From now on, forever, your cooking fires will burn their skins to a crisp.'

"So said that chief of the Little People. And so it is to this day," Ekashi was ending the story. "Always the skins of the fish we roast in the ashes of our fires come out scorched and hard.

"Well,"—the children's grandfather stroked his beard—"the Little People are gone now. But the Ainu also are disappearing. Soon no one will remember that this island of Hokkaido, once Yezo, was Ainu Land."

FRANCES CARPENTER has made two journeys around the world, and on a recent trip to Japan visited a model Ainu village on the northern island of Hokkaido. There, through an interpreter, she talked with the Ekashi, or the Old Man, and watched him lead his people through their delightful dances. She has written many books for young people, the most popular of which is *Tales of a Chinese Grandmother*. She now lives in Washington, D.C., where she was born.